It's another Quality Book from CGP

This book is for anyone doing GCSE Double Science at Higher Level.

Whatever subject you're doing it's the same
old story — there are lots of facts and you've just got
to learn them. KS4 Chemistry is no different.

Happily this CGP book gives you all that important
information as clearly and concisely as possible.

It's also got some daft bits in to try and make the whole
experience at least vaguely entertaining for you.

What CGP is all about

Our sole aim here at CGP is to produce the highest quality
books — carefully written, immaculately presented and
dangerously close to being funny.

Then we work our socks off to get them out to you
— at the cheapest possible prices.

Contents

Page References for Modular Syllabuses

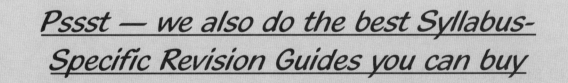

Published by Coordination Group Publications Ltd

Illustrations by Sandy Gardner e-mail: illustrations@sandygardner.co.uk

Updated by:
James Paul Wallis
Dominic Hall
Suzanne Worthington

ISBN 1 84146 502 X

With thanks to David Worthington, Eileen Worthington and Andy Park for the proofreading.

Groovy Website: www.cgpbooks.co.uk

Printed by Elanders Hindson, Newcastle upon Tyne.
Clipart source: CorelDRAW

Solids, Liquids and Gases

These are known as the <u>three states of matter</u>. Make sure you know everything there is to know.

Solids have Strong Forces of Attraction

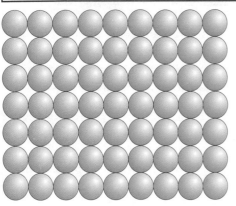

1) There are <u>strong forces</u> of attraction between molecules.
2) The molecules are held in <u>fixed positions</u> in a very regular <u>lattice arrangement</u>.
3) They <u>don't move</u> from their positions, so all solids keep a <u>definite shape</u> and <u>volume</u>, and don't flow like liquids.
4) They <u>vibrate</u> about their positions.
   The <u>hotter</u> the solid becomes, the <u>more</u> they vibrate.
   This causes solids to <u>expand</u> slightly when heated.
5) Solids <u>can't</u> be <u>compressed</u> because the molecules are already packed <u>very closely</u> together.
6) Solids are generally <u>very dense</u>.

Liquids have Moderate Forces of Attraction

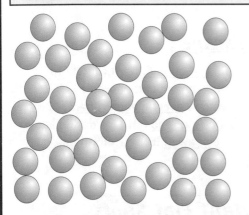

1) There is <u>some force</u> of attraction between the molecules.
2) The molecules are <u>free</u> to <u>move</u> past each other, but they do tend to <u>stick together</u>.
3) Liquids <u>don't</u> keep a <u>definite shape</u> and will flow to fill the bottom of a container. But they do keep the <u>same volume</u>.
4) The molecules are <u>constantly</u> moving in <u>random motion</u>.
   The <u>hotter</u> the liquid becomes, the <u>faster</u> they move.
   This causes liquids to <u>expand</u> slightly when heated.
5) Liquids <u>can't</u> be <u>compressed</u> because the molecules are already packed <u>closely together</u>.
6) Liquids are <u>quite dense</u>, but not as dense as solids.

Gases have No Forces of Attraction

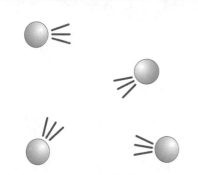

1) There is <u>no force</u> of attraction between the molecules.
2) The molecules are <u>free</u> to <u>move</u>. They travel in <u>straight lines</u> and only interact with each other <u>when they collide</u>.
3) Gases <u>don't</u> keep a definite <u>shape</u> or <u>volume</u> and will always <u>expand to fill</u> any container. Gases exert a <u>pressure</u> on the walls of the container.
4) The molecules are <u>constantly</u> moving in <u>random motion</u>.
   The <u>hotter</u> the gas becomes, the <u>faster</u> they move.
   When <u>heated</u>, a gas will either <u>expand</u> or its <u>pressure</u> will <u>increase</u>.
5) Gases can be <u>compressed</u> easily because there's <u>a lot of free space</u> between the molecules.
6) Gases all have <u>very low densities</u>.

Pressure exerted by molecules bouncing off the walls of the container.

Don't get yourself in a state about this lot, just learn it...

This is pretty basic stuff, but people still lose marks in the Exam because they don't make sure to learn all the little details really thoroughly. And there's only one way to do that: <u>COVER THE PAGE UP AND SCRIBBLE IT ALL DOWN FROM MEMORY</u>. That soon shows what you really know — and that's what you've got to do for every page. Do it now for this one, <u>AND KEEP TRYING UNTIL YOU GET IT ALL RIGHT</u>.

Changes of State

CHANGES OF STATE always involve HEAT ENERGY going either IN or OUT.

Melting — the rigid lattice breaks down

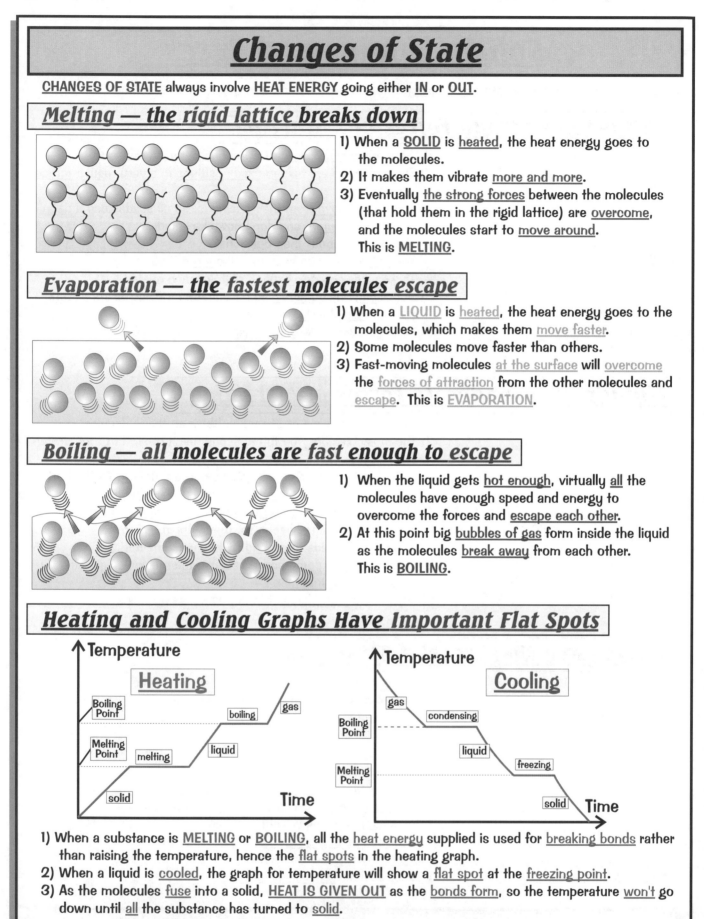

1) When a SOLID is heated, the heat energy goes to the molecules.
2) It makes them vibrate more and more.
3) Eventually the strong forces between the molecules (that hold them in the rigid lattice) are overcome, and the molecules start to move around. This is MELTING.

Evaporation — the fastest molecules escape

1) When a LIQUID is heated, the heat energy goes to the molecules, which makes them move faster.
2) Some molecules move faster than others.
3) Fast-moving molecules at the surface will overcome the forces of attraction from the other molecules and escape. This is EVAPORATION.

Boiling — all molecules are fast enough to escape

1) When the liquid gets hot enough, virtually all the molecules have enough speed and energy to overcome the forces and escape each other.
2) At this point big bubbles of gas form inside the liquid as the molecules break away from each other. This is BOILING.

Heating and Cooling Graphs Have Important Flat Spots

Heating

Temperature

Boiling Point
Melting Point
boiling
gas
liquid
melting
solid
Time

Cooling

Temperature

gas
condensing
Boiling Point
liquid
Melting Point
freezing
solid
Time

1) When a substance is MELTING or BOILING, all the heat energy supplied is used for breaking bonds rather than raising the temperature, hence the flat spots in the heating graph.
2) When a liquid is cooled, the graph for temperature will show a flat spot at the freezing point.
3) As the molecules fuse into a solid, HEAT IS GIVEN OUT as the bonds form, so the temperature won't go down until all the substance has turned to solid.

Revision — don't get all steamed up about it...

There are five diagrams and a total of 11 numbered points on this page. They wouldn't be there if you didn't need to learn them. So learn them. Then cover the page and scribble them all down. You have to realise this is the only way to really learn stuff properly. And learn it you must.

Atoms

The structure of atoms is real simple. I mean, gee, there's nothing to them. Just learn and enjoy.

The Nucleus

1) It's in the middle of the atom.
2) It contains protons and neutrons.
3) It has a positive charge because of the protons.
4) Almost the whole mass of the atom is concentrated in the nucleus.
5) But size-wise it's tiny compared to the atom as a whole.

The Electrons

1) Move around the nucleus.
2) They're negatively charged.
3) They're tiny, but they cover a lot of space.
4) The volume of their orbits determines how big the atom is.
5) They have virtually no mass.
6) They occupy shells around the nucleus.
7) These shells explain the whole of Chemistry.

Atoms are real tiny, don't forget.
They're too small to see, even with a microscope.

Number of Protons Equals Number of Electrons

1) Neutral atoms have no charge overall.
2) The charge on the electrons is the same size as the charge on the protons but opposite.
3) This means the number of protons always equals the number of electrons in a neutral atom.
4) If some electrons are added or removed, the atom becomes charged and is then an ion.
5) The number of neutrons isn't fixed but is usually just a bit higher than the number of protons.

Know Your Particles

Protons are Heavy and Positively Charged
Neutrons are Heavy and Neutral
Electrons are Tiny and Negatively Charged

PARTICLE	MASS	CHARGE
Proton	1	+1
Neutron	1	0
Electron	1/2000	-1

Basic Atom facts — they don't take up much space...

This stuff on atoms should be permanently engraved in the minds of everyone.
I don't understand how people can get through the day without knowing this stuff, really I don't.
Learn it now, and watch as the Universe unfolds and reveals its timeless mysteries to you...

Atomic Number and Mass Number

Come on. These are just two simple numbers for goodness' sake.
It just can't be that difficult to remember what they tell you about an atom.

The Mass Number
— Total of Protons and Neutrons

$^{23}_{11}$Na

The atomic Number
— Number of Protons

Points to Note
1) The atomic number tells you how many protons there are.
2) This also tells you how many electrons there are.
3) To get the number of neutrons — just subtract the atomic number from the mass number.
4) The mass number is always the biggest number. It tells you the relative mass of the atom.
5) The mass number is always roughly double the atomic number.
6) Which means there's about the same number of protons as neutrons in any nucleus.

Isotopes are the same except for an extra neutron or two

A favourite trick Exam question: "Explain what is meant by the term Isotope"
The trick is that it's impossible to explain what one isotope is.
You have to outsmart them and always start your answer "ISOTOPES ARE..."
LEARN the definition:

> Isotopes are: different atomic forms of the same element, which have
> the SAME number of PROTONS but a DIFFERENT number of NEUTRONS.

1) The upshot is: isotopes must have the same atomic number but different mass numbers.
2) If they had different atomic numbers, they'd be different elements altogether.
3) A very popular pair of isotopes are carbon-12 and carbon-14.

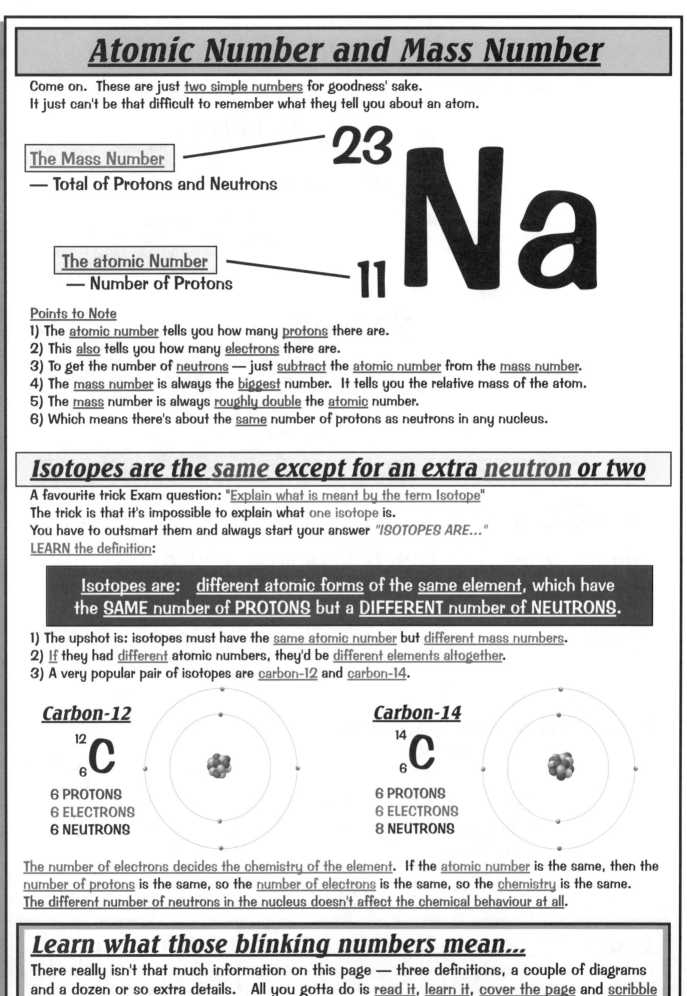

Carbon-12
$^{12}_{6}$C

6 PROTONS
6 ELECTRONS
6 NEUTRONS

Carbon-14
$^{14}_{6}$C

6 PROTONS
6 ELECTRONS
8 NEUTRONS

The number of electrons decides the chemistry of the element. If the atomic number is the same, then the number of protons is the same, so the number of electrons is the same, so the chemistry is the same. The different number of neutrons in the nucleus doesn't affect the chemical behaviour at all.

Learn what those blinking numbers mean...

There really isn't that much information on this page — three definitions, a couple of diagrams and a dozen or so extra details.   All you gotta do is read it, learn it, cover the page and scribble it all down again. Smile and enjoy.

Electron Shells and Ionic Bonding

The fact that electrons occupy "shells" around the nucleus is what causes the whole of chemistry. Remember that, and watch how it applies to each bit of it. It's ace.

Electron Shell Rules:

1) Electrons always occupy <u>shells</u> or <u>energy levels</u>.

2) The <u>lowest</u> energy levels are <u>always filled first</u>.

3) Only <u>a certain number</u> of electrons are allowed in each shell:
<u>1st shell</u>: 2   <u>2nd Shell</u>: 8   <u>3rd Shell</u>: 8

4) Atoms are much <u>happier</u> when they have <u>full electron shells</u>.

5) In most atoms the <u>outer shell</u> is <u>not full</u> and this makes the atom want to <u>react</u>.

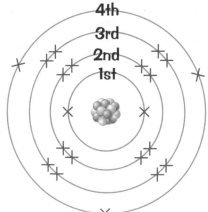

4th shell still filling

Ionic Bonding — Swapping Electrons

In <u>ionic bonding</u>, atoms <u>lose or gain electrons</u> to form <u>charged particles</u> (ions) which are then <u>strongly attracted</u> to one another, (because of the attraction of opposite charges, + and –).

A shell with just one electron is well keen to get rid...

<u>All</u> the atoms over at the <u>left hand side</u> of the periodic table, such as <u>sodium, potassium, calcium</u> etc. have just <u>one or two electrons</u> in their outer shell. And basically they're <u>pretty keen to get shot of them</u>, because then they'll only have <u>full shells</u> left, which is how they <u>like</u> it.
So given half a chance they do get rid, and that leaves the atom as an <u>ion</u> instead.
Now ions aren't the kind of things that sit around quietly watching the world go by.
They tend to <u>leap</u> at the first passing ion with an <u>opposite charge</u> and stick to it like glue.

A nearly full shell is well keen to get that extra electron...

On the <u>other side</u> of the periodic table, the elements in <u>Group Six</u> and <u>Group Seven</u>, such as <u>oxygen</u> and <u>chlorine</u> have outer shells which are <u>nearly full</u>. They're obviously pretty keen to <u>gain</u> that <u>extra one or two electrons</u> to fill the shell up. When they do of course they become <u>ions</u>, you know, not the kind of things to sit around, and before you know it, <u>pop</u>, they've latched onto the atom (ion) that gave up the electron a moment earlier. The reaction of sodium and chlorine is a <u>classic case</u>:

The <u>chlorine</u> atom <u>picks up</u> the <u>spare electron</u> and becomes a Cl $^-$ ion.

POP!

The <u>sodium</u> atom <u>gives up</u> its <u>outer electron</u> and becomes an Na$^+$ ion.

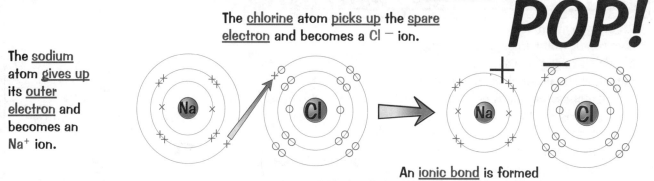

An <u>ionic bond</u> is formed

Full Shells — it's the name of the game, pal...

There's quite a lot of words on this page but only to hammer home three very basic points:
1) Electrons have shells — with rules   2) Ionic bonds involve swapping electrons
3) Some atoms like to lose them, some like to gain them. <u>Learn all the highlighted bits.</u>

Covalent Bonding

Covalent Bonds — Sharing Electrons

1) <u>Sometimes</u> atoms prefer to make <u>covalent bonds</u> by <u>sharing electrons</u> with other atoms.
2) This way <u>both atoms</u> feel that they have <u>a full outer shell</u>, and that makes them happy.
3) <u>Each</u> covalent bond provides <u>one extra</u> shared electron for each atom.
4) Each atom involved has to make <u>enough</u> covalent bonds to <u>fill up</u> its outer shell.
5) <u>Learn</u> these <u>five</u> important examples:

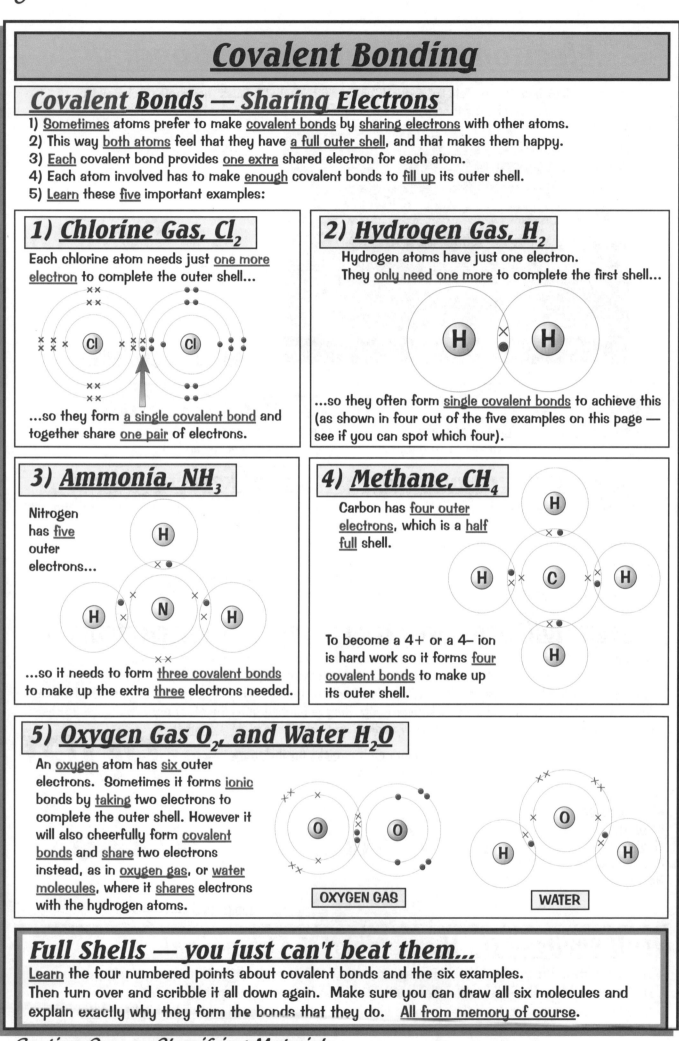

1) Chlorine Gas, Cl_2

Each chlorine atom needs just <u>one more</u> <u>electron</u> to complete the outer shell...

...so they form <u>a single covalent bond</u> and together share <u>one pair</u> of electrons.

2) Hydrogen Gas, H_2

Hydrogen atoms have just one electron. They <u>only need one more</u> to complete the first shell...

...so they often form <u>single covalent bonds</u> to achieve this (as shown in four out of the five examples on this page — see if you can spot which four).

3) Ammonia, NH_3

Nitrogen has <u>five</u> outer electrons...

...so it needs to form <u>three covalent bonds</u> to make up the extra <u>three</u> electrons needed.

4) Methane, CH_4

Carbon has <u>four outer</u> <u>electrons</u>, which is a <u>half</u> <u>full</u> shell.

To become a 4+ or a 4– ion is hard work so it forms <u>four</u> <u>covalent bonds</u> to make up its outer shell.

5) Oxygen Gas O_2, and Water H_2O

An <u>oxygen</u> atom has <u>six</u> outer electrons. Sometimes it forms <u>ionic</u> bonds by <u>taking</u> two electrons to complete the outer shell. However it will also cheerfully form <u>covalent</u> <u>bonds</u> and <u>share</u> two electrons instead, as in <u>oxygen gas</u>, or <u>water</u> <u>molecules</u>, where it <u>shares</u> electrons with the hydrogen atoms.

OXYGEN GAS

WATER

Full Shells — you just can't beat them...

<u>Learn</u> the four numbered points about covalent bonds and the six examples.
Then turn over and scribble it all down again. Make sure you can draw all six molecules and explain exactly why they form the bonds that they do. <u>All from memory of course</u>.

Ionic Substances

Simple Ions — Groups 1 & 2 and 6 & 7

1) The elements that most readily form <u>ions</u> are those in Groups 1, 2, 6, and 7.

2) <u>Group 1 and 2 elements</u> are <u>metals</u> and they <u>lose</u> electrons to form <u>+ve ions</u> or <u>cations</u>.

3) <u>Group 6 and 7 elements</u> are <u>non-metals</u>. They <u>gain</u> electrons to form <u>−ve ions</u> or <u>anions</u>.

4) Make sure you know these easy ones:

Cations		Anions	
Gr I	Gr II	Gr VI	Gr VII
Li^+	Be^{2+}	O^{2-}	F^-
Na^+	Mg^{2+}		Cl^-
K^+	Ca^{2+}		

5) When any of the above elements <u>react together</u>, they form <u>ionic bonds</u>.

6) Only elements at <u>opposite sides</u> of the periodic table will form ionic bonds, e.g. Na and Cl, where one of them becomes a <u>cation</u> (+ve) and one becomes an <u>anion</u> (−ve).

Remember, the + and − charges we talk about, e.g. Na^+ for sodium, just tell you <u>what type of ion the atom WILL FORM</u> in a chemical reaction. In sodium <u>metal</u> there are <u>only neutral sodium atoms, Na</u>. The Na^+ ions <u>will only appear</u> if the sodium metal <u>reacts</u> with something like water or chlorine.

Giant Ionic Structures don't melt easily, but when they do...

1) <u>Ionic bonds</u> always produce <u>giant ionic structures</u>.

2) The ions form a <u>closely packed regular lattice</u> arrangement.

3) There are <u>very strong chemical bonds</u> between <u>all</u> the ions.

4) A single crystal of salt is <u>one giant ionic lattice</u>, which is why salt crystals tend to be cuboid in shape:

1) They have <u>High melting points and boiling points</u>

due to the <u>very strong</u> chemical bonds between <u>all the ions</u> in the giant structure.

2) They <u>Dissolve to form solutions that conduct electricity</u>

When <u>dissolved</u> the ions <u>separate</u> and are all <u>free to move</u> in the solution, so obviously they'll <u>carry electric current</u>.

Dissolved in Water
Melted

3) They <u>Conduct electricity when molten</u>

When it <u>melts</u>, the ions are <u>free to move</u> and they'll carry electric current.

Giant Structures — like salt crystals? You betcha...

<u>Learn</u> which atoms form 1+, 1-, 2+ and 2- ions, and why (see P. 5). Then learn all the features of ionic solids. When you think you know it all, <u>cover the page</u> and start scribbling to see what you do know. Then look back, <u>learn the bits you missed</u>, and <u>try again</u>. And again.

Covalent Substances: Two Kinds

Substances formed from <u>covalent bonds</u> can either be <u>simple molecules</u> or <u>giant structures</u>.

Simple Molecular Substances

1) The atoms form <u>very strong covalent bonds</u> to form <u>small molecules</u> of several atoms.
2) By contrast, the forces of attraction <u>between</u> these molecules are <u>very weak</u>.
3) The <u>result</u> of these <u>feeble inter-molecular forces</u> is that the melting- and boiling-points are <u>very low</u>, because the molecules are <u>easily parted</u> from each other.
4) Most molecular substances are <u>gases or liquids</u> at room temperature.
5) Molecular substances <u>don't conduct electricity</u>, simply because there are <u>no ions</u>.
6) They <u>don't dissolve in water</u>, usually.
7) You can usually tell a molecular substance just from its <u>physical state</u>, which is always kinda "<u>mushy</u>" — i.e. <u>liquid</u> or <u>gas</u> or an <u>easily-melted solid</u>.

Buckminster Fullerene

1) 60 carbon atoms joined in a big ball.
2) Each carbon atom forms three covalent bonds.

Very weak inter-molecular forces

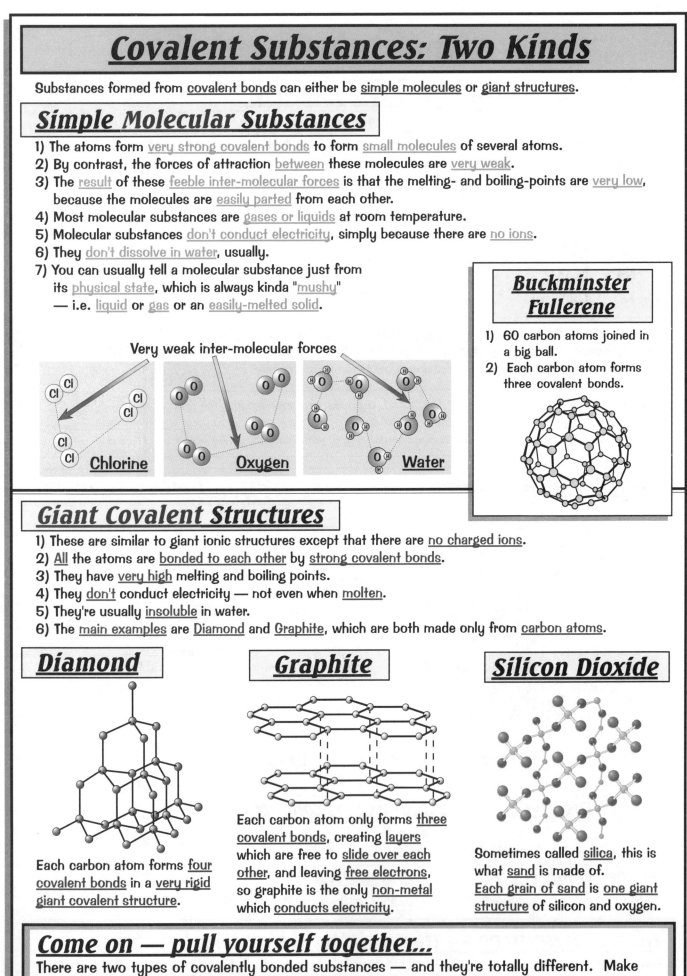

Chlorine

Oxygen

Water

Giant Covalent Structures

1) These are similar to giant ionic structures except that there are <u>no charged ions</u>.
2) <u>All</u> the atoms are <u>bonded to each other</u> by <u>strong covalent bonds</u>.
3) They have <u>very high</u> melting and boiling points.
4) They <u>don't</u> conduct electricity — not even when <u>molten</u>.
5) They're usually <u>insoluble</u> in water.
6) The <u>main examples</u> are <u>Diamond</u> and <u>Graphite</u>, which are both made only from <u>carbon atoms</u>.

Diamond

Each carbon atom forms <u>four covalent bonds</u> in a <u>very rigid giant covalent structure</u>.

Graphite

Each carbon atom only forms <u>three covalent bonds</u>, creating <u>layers</u> which are free to <u>slide over each other</u>, and leaving <u>free electrons</u>, so graphite is the only <u>non-metal</u> which <u>conducts electricity</u>.

Silicon Dioxide

Sometimes called <u>silica</u>, this is what <u>sand</u> is made of.
Each grain of sand is <u>one giant structure</u> of silicon and oxygen.

Come on — pull yourself together...

There are two types of covalently bonded substances — and they're totally different. Make sure you know all the details about them, and the examples too. <u>This is real basic stuff</u> — just easy marks to be won... or lost. <u>Cover the page</u> and see how many marks you're gonna <u>win</u>.

Metallic Structures

Metal Properties are all due to the Sea of Free Electrons

1) <u>Metals</u> also consist of a <u>giant structure</u>.

2) <u>Metallic bonds</u> involve the all-important "<u>free electrons</u>", which produce <u>all</u> the properties of metals. These free electrons come from the <u>outer shell</u> of <u>every</u> metal atom in the structure.

3) These electrons are <u>free to move</u> and so metals <u>conduct heat and electricity</u>.

4) These electrons also <u>hold the atoms together</u> in a regular structure.

5) They also allow the atoms to <u>slide over each</u> other causing metals to be <u>malleable</u> (which means you can do useful things with them, like roll them into sheets).

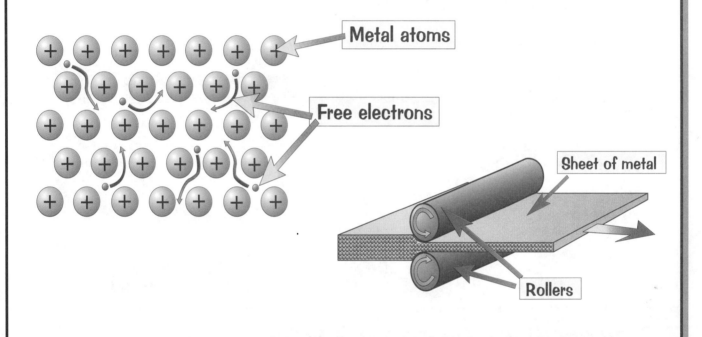

Metal atoms

Free electrons

Sheet of metal

Rollers

Identifying the bonding in a substance by its properties

If you've learnt the properties of the <u>four types</u> of substance properly, together with their <u>names</u> of course, then you should be able to easily <u>identify</u> most substances just by the way they <u>behave</u> as either: <u>ionic</u>, <u>giant-covalent</u>, <u>simple molecular covalent</u>, or <u>metallic</u>. The way they're likely to test you in the Exam is by describing the <u>physical properties</u> of a substance and asking you to decide <u>which type of bonding</u> it has and therefore what type of material it is. If you know your onions you'll have no trouble at all. If not, you're gonna struggle.

Bonding — where would we all be without it...

A good approach here is the <u>mini-essay method</u>, where you just write down everything you can about each section, and then look back to see what you missed. This is much better than trying to remember the numbered points in the right order. <u>Try it for all the types of bonding</u>.

Elements, Compounds and Mixtures

You'd better be sure you know the <u>subtle differences</u> between these.

Elements consist of one type of atom only

Quite a lot of everyday substances are <u>elements</u>:

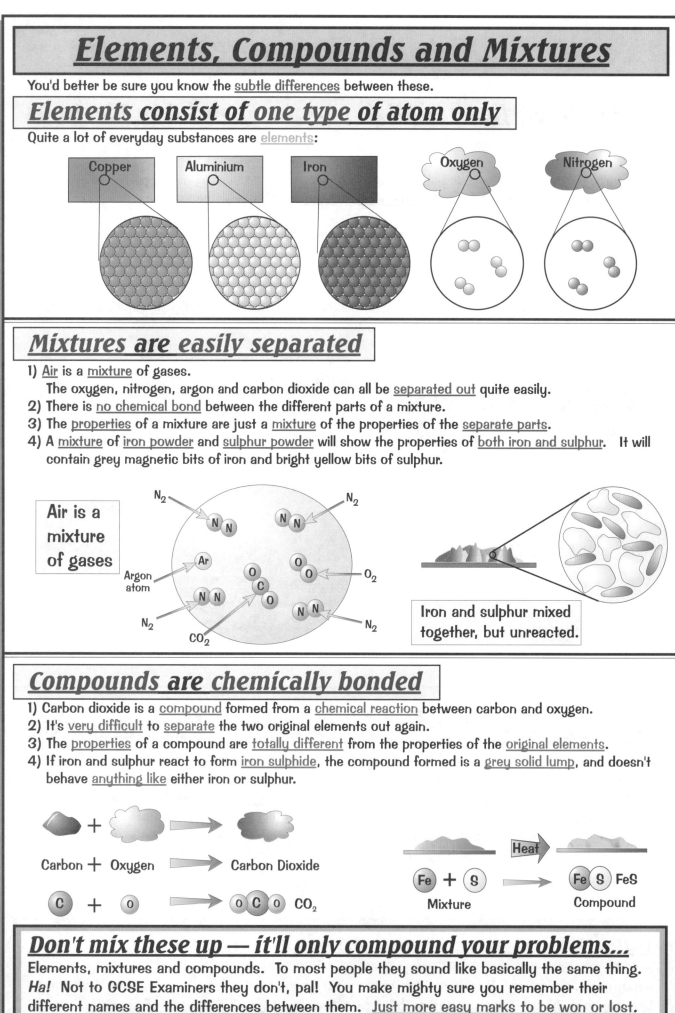

Mixtures are easily separated

1) <u>Air</u> is a <u>mixture</u> of gases.
   The oxygen, nitrogen, argon and carbon dioxide can all be <u>separated out</u> quite easily.
2) There is <u>no chemical bond</u> between the different parts of a mixture.
3) The <u>properties</u> of a mixture are just a <u>mixture</u> of the properties of the <u>separate parts</u>.
4) A <u>mixture</u> of <u>iron powder</u> and <u>sulphur powder</u> will show the properties of <u>both iron and sulphur</u>. It will contain grey magnetic bits of iron and bright yellow bits of sulphur.

Air is a mixture of gases

Iron and sulphur mixed together, but unreacted.

Compounds are chemically bonded

1) Carbon dioxide is a <u>compound</u> formed from a <u>chemical reaction</u> between carbon and oxygen.
2) It's <u>very difficult</u> to <u>separate</u> the two original elements out again.
3) The <u>properties</u> of a compound are <u>totally different</u> from the properties of the <u>original elements</u>.
4) If iron and sulphur react to form <u>iron sulphide</u>, the compound formed is a <u>grey solid lump</u>, and doesn't behave <u>anything like</u> either iron or sulphur.

Carbon + Oxygen → Carbon Dioxide

C + O → CO_2

Mixture   Heat   Compound

Fe + S → Fe S FeS

Don't mix these up — it'll only compound your problems...

Elements, mixtures and compounds. To most people they sound like basically the same thing. *Ha!* Not to GCSE Examiners they don't, pal! You make mighty sure you remember their different names and the differences between them. <u>Just more easy marks to be won or lost</u>.

Common Tests and Hazard Symbols

You need to know these <u>six easy lab tests</u>:

1) *Chlorine bleaches damp litmus paper*

(i.e. it <u>turns it white</u>).

2) *Oxygen relights a glowing splint*

The standard test for <u>oxygen</u> is that it <u>relights a glowing splint</u>.

3) *Carbon dioxide turns limewater milky*

<u>Carbon dioxide</u> can be detected by <u>turning limewater cloudy</u> when it's bubbled through.

4) *The three lab tests for Water*

Water can be detected in three ways:
a) by its <u>boiling point</u> of <u>100ºC</u>
b) by turning <u>white anhydrous copper sulphate</u> to <u>blue hydrated copper sulphate</u> (and getting hot)
c) by turning <u>anhydrous cobalt chloride paper</u> from <u>blue</u> to <u>pink</u>.

5) *Lab test for Hydrogen — the notorious "Squeaky pop"*

Just bring a <u>lighted splint</u> near the gas with air around.
If it's hydrogen it'll make a "<u>squeaky pop</u>" as it burns with the oxygen in the air to form H_2O.

You need to know the test for alkenes as well — see page 16.

Hazard Symbols

The official hazard symbol for "harmful" and "irritant" is a black cross. Some products add an "h" or "i" to show the difference.

Oxidising
<u>Provides oxygen</u> which allows other materials to <u>burn more fiercely</u>.
<u>Example:</u> Liquid Oxygen.

Highly Flammable
<u>Catches fire</u> easily.
<u>Example:</u> Petrol.

Toxic
<u>Can cause death</u> either by swallowing, breathing in, or absorption through the skin. <u>Example:</u> Cyanide.

Harmful
Similar to toxic but <u>not quite as dangerous</u>.
<u>Example:</u> Petrol, meths.

Irritant
Not corrosive but <u>can cause reddening or blistering of the skin</u>.
<u>Examples:</u> Bleach, children, etc.

Corrosive
<u>Attacks and destroys living tissues</u>, including eyes and skin.
<u>Example:</u> Sulphuric acid.

Learn the Six Lab Tests — easy as squeaky pop...

This is pretty basic stuff, but people still lose marks in the Exam because they don't make sure to learn all the little details really thoroughly. That's true for just about everything in this book. It's no good just letting your eyes drift lazily across the page and thinking "Oh yeah, I know all that stuff". You've gotta really make sure you <u>do</u> know it all. <u>And there's only one way to do that</u> — so do it now.

Revision Summary for Section One

These certainly aren't the easiest questions you're going to come across. That's because they test what you know without giving you any clues. At first you might think they're impossibly difficult. Eventually you'll realise that they simply test whether you've learnt the stuff or not.
If you're struggling to answer these then you need to do some serious learning.

1) What are the three states of matter?

2) Describe the bonding and atom spacing in all three states.

3) Describe the physical properties of each of these three states of matter.

4) What are the ways of changing between the three states of matter?

5) Explain what goes on in all three processes, in terms of bonds and heat energy.

6) Sketch a heating graph and a cooling graph, with lots of labels.

7) Explain why these graphs have flat spots.

8) Sketch an atom. Give five details about the nucleus and five details about the electrons.

9) What are the three particles found in an atom?

10) Do a table showing their relative masses and charges.

11) How do the numbers of these particles compare to each other in a neutral atom?

12) What do the mass number and atomic number represent?

13) Explain what an isotope is. (!) Give a well-known example.

14) List five facts (or "Rules") about electron shells.

15) What is ionic bonding? Which kind of atoms like to do ionic bonding?

16) Why do atoms want to form ionic bonds anyway?

17) What is covalent bonding? Which kind of atoms tend to do covalent bonding?

18) Why do some atoms do covalent bonding instead of ionic bonding?

19) Give five examples of covalent molecules, and sketch diagrams, showing the electrons.

20) What kind of ions are formed by elements in Groups I and II, and those in Groups VI and VII?

21) Draw a diagram of a giant ionic lattice and give three features of giant ionic structures.

22) List the three main properties of ionic compounds.

23) What are the two types of covalent substances? Give three examples of each type.

24) Give three physical properties for each of the two types of covalent substance.

25) Explain how the bonding in each type of covalent substance causes its physical properties.

26) What is special about the bonding in metals?

27) List the three main properties of metals and explain how the metallic bonding causes them.

28) What is the difference between elements, mixtures and compounds?

29) Give three examples each of elements, mixtures and compounds.

30) Give full details of the lab tests for:
   Chlorine, oxygen, carbon dioxide, water (3), hydrogen.

31) Sketch the six Hazard Symbols, explain what they mean, and give an example for each.

Section One — Classifying Materials

Fractional Distillation of Crude Oil

1) <u>Crude oil</u> is formed from the buried remains of plants and animals — it's a fossil fuel. Over millions of years, with high temperature and pressure, the remains turn to crude oil which can be drilled up.
2) Crude oil is a <u>mixture</u> of <u>hydrocarbons</u> of different sized molecules.
3) <u>Hydrocarbons</u> are basically <u>fuels</u> such as petrol and diesel. They're made of just carbon and hydrogen.
4) The <u>bigger</u> and <u>longer</u> the molecules, the <u>less runny</u> the hydrocarbon (fuel) is.
5) <u>Fractional distillation</u> splits crude oil up into its separate <u>fractions</u>.
6) The <u>shorter</u> the molecules, the <u>lower</u> the <u>temperature</u> at which that fraction <u>condenses</u>.

Crude Oil is Split into Separate Hydrocarbons (fuels)

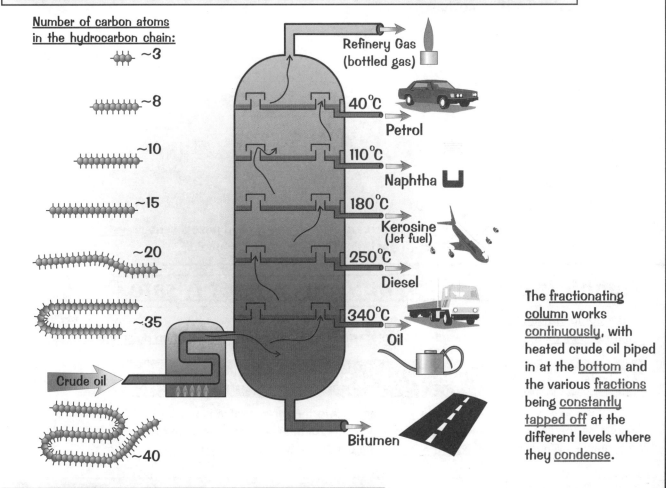

Number of carbon atoms in the hydrocarbon chain:

~3

~8

~10

~15

~20

~35

~40

Refinery Gas (bottled gas)

40°C — Petrol

110°C — Naphtha

180°C — Kerosine (Jet fuel)

250°C — Diesel

340°C — Oil

Crude oil

Bitumen

The <u>fractionating column</u> works <u>continuously</u>, with heated crude oil piped in at the <u>bottom</u> and the various <u>fractions</u> being <u>constantly tapped off</u> at the different levels where they <u>condense</u>.

Crude oil is a very big part of modern life

1) There's a <u>massive industry</u> with scientists working to find oil reserves, take it out of the ground, and turn it into useful products.
2) It provides the <u>fuel</u> for most modern transport.
3) It also provides the <u>raw materials</u> for making various <u>chemicals</u> including <u>plastics</u>. Plastics are just ace, of course. The world without plastics? Why, it would be the end of civilisation as we know it...
4) Oil can be serious bad news for the <u>environment</u>. Oil slicks at sea, old engine oil down the drain, plastics that won't rot if you throw them away... <u>Some</u> things can be <u>recycled</u> though, which helps.

Revising for oil — you know the drill...

A typical question would show a fractionating column and ask you which bit you'd expect petrol or diesel to come out of, or ask you how long the carbon chain of diesel is, or ask you to give the main uses of crude oil. So make sure you know <u>all</u> the details. When you think you do, <u>cover up the page</u> and <u>scribble down</u> all the details including the diagram. <u>Then try again.</u>

Using Hydrocarbons

Hydrocarbons are long chain molecules

As the size of the hydrocarbon molecule increases:

1) The boiling point increases

2) It gets less flammable
(doesn't set fire so easy)

Heat   Heat

3) It gets more viscous
(doesn't flow so easy)

4) It gets less volatile
(i.e. doesn't evaporate so easily)

The vapours of the more volatile hydrocarbons are very flammable and pose a serious fire risk.
So don't smoke at the petrol station. (In fact, don't smoke at all, it's stupid.)

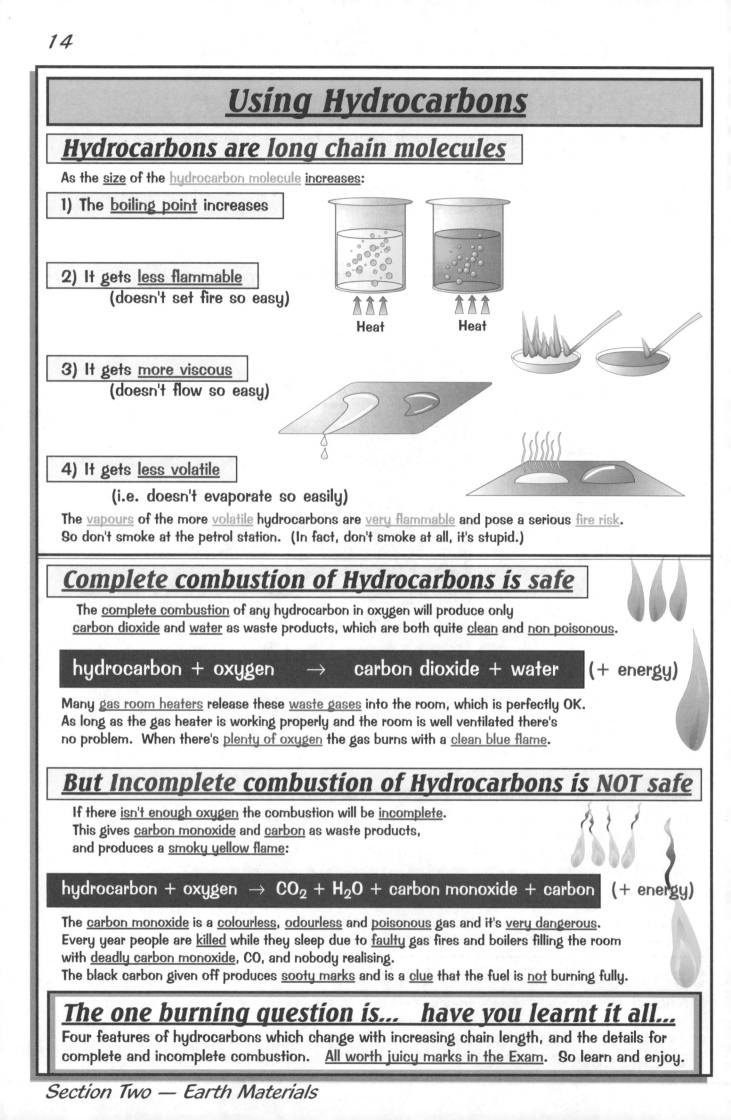

Complete combustion of Hydrocarbons is safe

The complete combustion of any hydrocarbon in oxygen will produce only
carbon dioxide and water as waste products, which are both quite clean and non poisonous.

hydrocarbon + oxygen → carbon dioxide + water (+ energy)

Many gas room heaters release these waste gases into the room, which is perfectly OK.
As long as the gas heater is working properly and the room is well ventilated there's
no problem. When there's plenty of oxygen the gas burns with a clean blue flame.

But Incomplete combustion of Hydrocarbons is NOT safe

If there isn't enough oxygen the combustion will be incomplete.
This gives carbon monoxide and carbon as waste products,
and produces a smoky yellow flame:

hydrocarbon + oxygen → CO_2 + H_2O + carbon monoxide + carbon (+ energy)

The carbon monoxide is a colourless, odourless and poisonous gas and it's very dangerous.
Every year people are killed while they sleep due to faulty gas fires and boilers filling the room
with deadly carbon monoxide, CO, and nobody realising.
The black carbon given off produces sooty marks and is a clue that the fuel is not burning fully.

The one burning question is... have you learnt it all...

Four features of hydrocarbons which change with increasing chain length, and the details for
complete and incomplete combustion. All worth juicy marks in the Exam. So learn and enjoy.

$$\boxed{C_n H_{2n} + 2}$$

Cracking Hydrocarbons

Cracking — splitting up long chain hydrocarbons

1) Long chain hydrocarbons form thick gloopy liquids like tar which aren't all that useful.
2) The process called cracking turns them into shorter molecules which are much more useful.

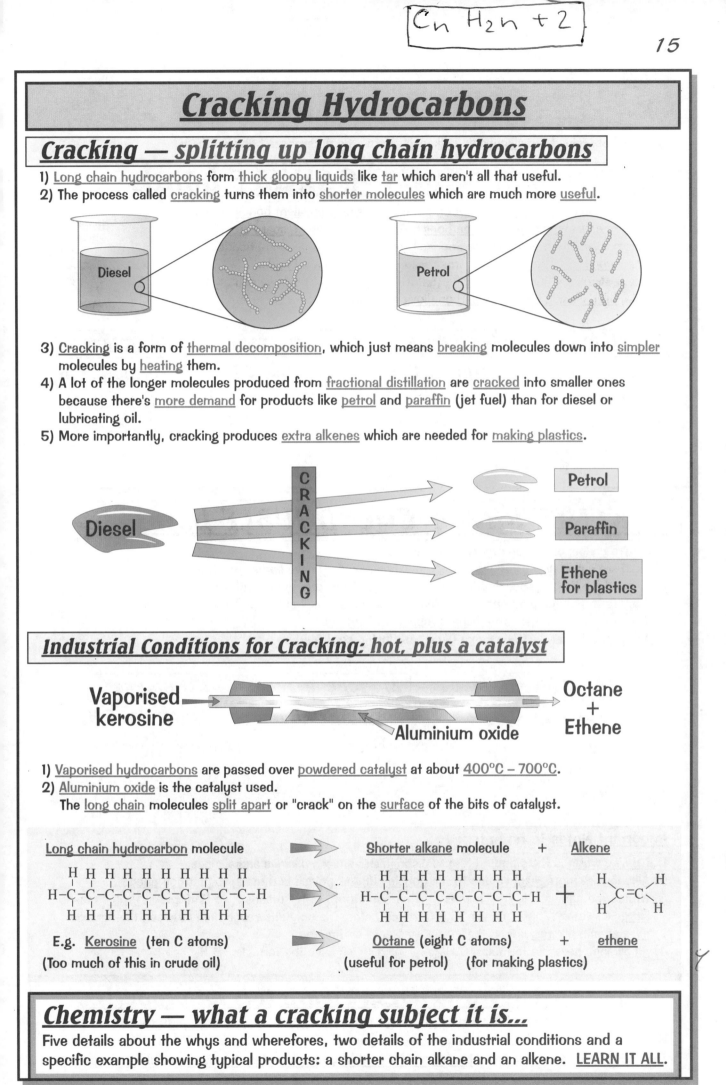

3) Cracking is a form of thermal decomposition, which just means breaking molecules down into simpler molecules by heating them.
4) A lot of the longer molecules produced from fractional distillation are cracked into smaller ones because there's more demand for products like petrol and paraffin (jet fuel) than for diesel or lubricating oil.
5) More importantly, cracking produces extra alkenes which are needed for making plastics.

Industrial Conditions for Cracking: hot, plus a catalyst

1) Vaporised hydrocarbons are passed over powdered catalyst at about 400°C – 700°C.
2) Aluminium oxide is the catalyst used.
   The long chain molecules split apart or "crack" on the surface of the bits of catalyst.

Long chain hydrocarbon molecule ⟹ Shorter alkane molecule + Alkene

E.g. Kerosine (ten C atoms) ⟹ Octane (eight C atoms) + ethene
(Too much of this in crude oil) (useful for petrol) (for making plastics)

Chemistry — what a cracking subject it is...

Five details about the whys and wherefores, two details of the industrial conditions and a specific example showing typical products: a shorter chain alkane and an alkene. LEARN IT ALL.

Alkanes and Alkenes

Crude oil contains both alkanes and alkenes. Know the differences between them.

ALKANES have all C–C SINGLE bonds

1) They're made up of chains of carbon atoms with single covalent bonds between them.
2) They're called saturated hydrocarbons because they have no spare bonds left.
3) This is also why they don't decolourise bromine water — no spare bonds.
4) They won't form polymers — same reason again, no spare bonds.
5) The first four alkanes are methane (natural gas), ethane, propane and butane.
6) They burn cleanly producing carbon dioxide and water.

Bromine water
+ alkane
— still brown.

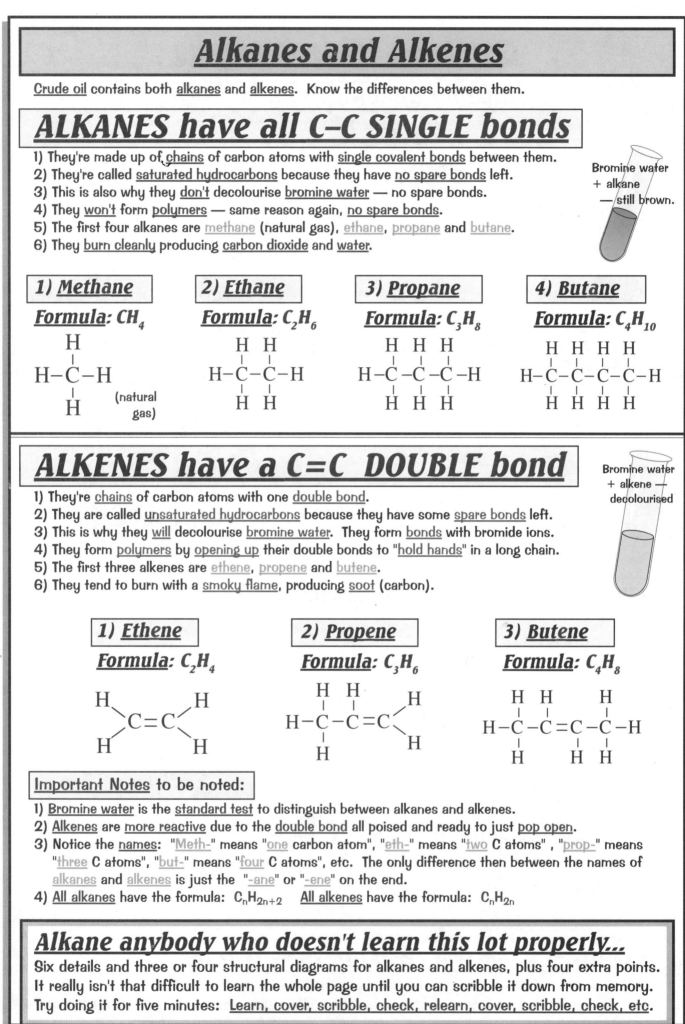

1) Methane
Formula: CH_4

H–C–H (natural gas)

2) Ethane
Formula: C_2H_6

H–C–C–H

3) Propane
Formula: C_3H_8

H–C–C–C–H

4) Butane
Formula: C_4H_{10}

H–C–C–C–C–H

ALKENES have a C=C DOUBLE bond

Bromine water
+ alkene —
decolourised

1) They're chains of carbon atoms with one double bond.
2) They are called unsaturated hydrocarbons because they have some spare bonds left.
3) This is why they will decolourise bromine water. They form bonds with bromide ions.
4) They form polymers by opening up their double bonds to "hold hands" in a long chain.
5) The first three alkenes are ethene, propene and butene.
6) They tend to burn with a smoky flame, producing soot (carbon).

1) Ethene
Formula: C_2H_4

C=C

2) Propene
Formula: C_3H_6

H–C–C=C

3) Butene
Formula: C_4H_8

H–C–C=C–C–H

Important Notes to be noted:

1) Bromine water is the standard test to distinguish between alkanes and alkenes.
2) Alkenes are more reactive due to the double bond all poised and ready to just pop open.
3) Notice the names: "Meth-" means "one carbon atom", "eth-" means "two C atoms", "prop-" means "three C atoms", "but-" means "four C atoms", etc. The only difference then between the names of alkanes and alkenes is just the "-ane" or "-ene" on the end.
4) All alkanes have the formula: C_nH_{2n+2} All alkenes have the formula: C_nH_{2n}

Alkane anybody who doesn't learn this lot properly...

Six details and three or four structural diagrams for alkanes and alkenes, plus four extra points.
It really isn't that difficult to learn the whole page until you can scribble it down from memory.
Try doing it for five minutes: Learn, cover, scribble, check, relearn, cover, scribble, check, etc.

Polymers and Plastics

Polymers and plastics were first discovered in about 1933. By 1970 it was all too late. Those halcyon days when they made proper motor cars with leather seats and lovely wooden dashboards, were over. Sigh.

Alkenes open their double bonds to form Polymers

Under a bit of <u>pressure</u> and with a bit of a <u>catalyst</u> to help it along, many <u>small alkenes</u> will open up their <u>double bonds</u> and "join hands" (polymerisation) to form <u>very long chains</u> called <u>polymers</u>.
<u>Ethene</u> becoming polyethene or "polythene", is the easiest example:

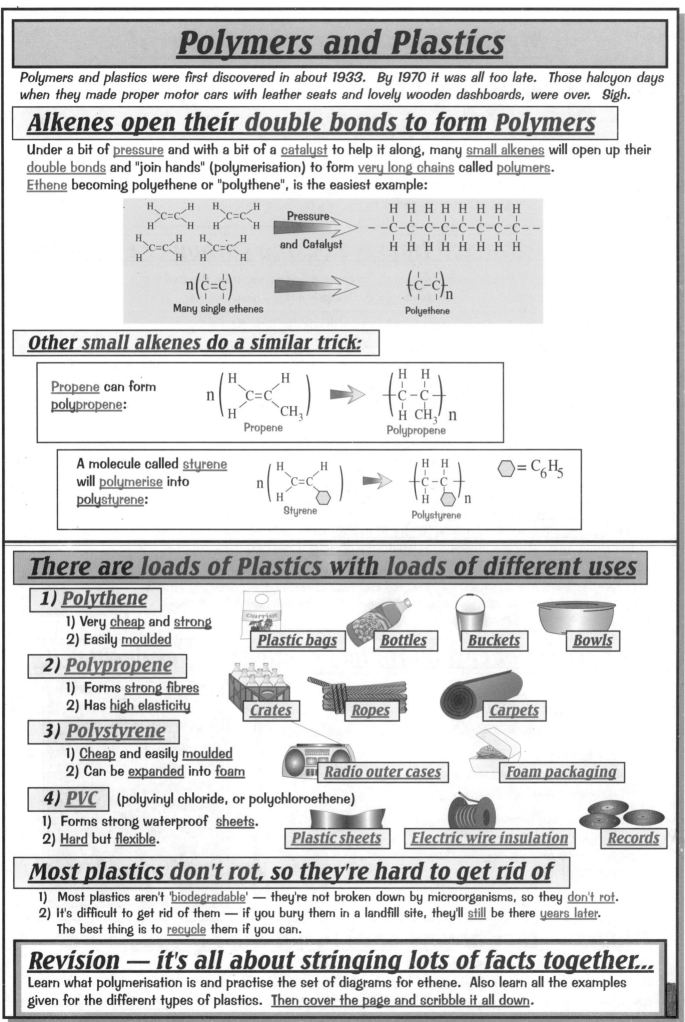

Other small alkenes do a similar trick:

<u>Propene</u> can form <u>polypropene</u>:

A molecule called <u>styrene</u> will <u>polymerise</u> into <u>polystyrene</u>:

$\bigcirc = C_6H_5$

There are loads of Plastics with loads of different uses

1) Polythene
1) Very <u>cheap</u> and <u>strong</u>
2) Easily <u>moulded</u>

Plastic bags *Bottles* *Buckets* *Bowls*

2) Polypropene
1) Forms <u>strong fibres</u>
2) Has <u>high elasticity</u>

Crates *Ropes* *Carpets*

3) Polystyrene
1) <u>Cheap</u> and easily <u>moulded</u>
2) Can be <u>expanded</u> into <u>foam</u>

Radio outer cases *Foam packaging*

4) PVC (polyvinyl chloride, or polychloroethene)
1) Forms strong waterproof <u>sheets</u>.
2) <u>Hard</u> but <u>flexible</u>.

Plastic sheets *Electric wire insulation* *Records*

Most plastics don't rot, so they're hard to get rid of

1) Most plastics aren't 'biodegradable' — they're not broken down by microorganisms, so they <u>don't rot</u>.
2) It's difficult to get rid of them — if you bury them in a landfill site, they'll <u>still</u> be there <u>years later</u>.
   The best thing is to <u>recycle</u> them if you can.

Revision — it's all about stringing lots of facts together...

Learn what polymerisation is and practise the set of diagrams for ethene. Also learn all the examples given for the different types of plastics. <u>Then cover the page and scribble it all down.</u>

Metal Ores From the Ground

Rocks, Minerals and Ores

1) A rock is a mixture of minerals.
2) A mineral is any solid element or compound found naturally in the Earth's crust.
   Examples: Diamond (carbon), quartz (silicon dioxide), bauxite (Al_2O_3).
3) A metal ore is defined as a mineral or minerals which contain enough metal in them to make it worthwhile extracting the metal from it.
4) There's a limited amount of minerals and ores — they're "finite resources".

Metals are extracted from ores using Carbon or Electrolysis

1) Extracting a metal from its ore involves a chemical reaction to separate the metal out.
2) In many cases the metal is found as an oxide. There are three ores you need to know:

> a) Iron ore is called Haematite, which is iron(III) oxide, formula Fe_2O_3.
> b) Aluminium ore is called Bauxite, which is aluminium oxide, formula Al_2O_3.
> c) Copper ore is called Malachite, which is copper(II) carbonate, formula $CuCO_3$.

3) The two common ways of extracting a metal from its ore are:
   a) Chemical reduction using carbon or carbon monoxide
   b) Electrolysis
4) Gold is one of the few metals found as a metal rather than in a chemical compound (an ore).

More Reactive Metals are Harder to Get

1) The more reactive metals took longer to be discovered. (e.g. aluminium, sodium)
2) The more reactive metals are also harder to extract from their mineral ores.
3) The above two facts are obviously related. It's obvious when you think about it...

Even primitive folk could find gold easy enough just by scrabbling about in streams, and then melt it into ingots and jewellery and statues of ABBA during their 1857 comeback tour, but coming up with a fully operational electrolysis plant to extract sodium metal from rock salt, complete with plastic yukkas in the foyer, just by paddling about a bit... unlikely.

The Position of Carbon In the Reactivity Series decides it...

1) Metals higher than carbon in the reactivity series have to be extracted using electrolysis.

2) Metals below carbon in the reactivity series can be extracted by reduction using carbon.

3) This is obviously because carbon can only take the oxygen away from metals which are less reactive than carbon itself is.

Extracted using Electrolysis

Extracted by reduction using carbon

The Reactivity Series	
Potassium	K
Sodium	Na
Calcium	Ca
Magnesium	Mg
Aluminium	Al
CARBON	C
Zinc	Zn
Iron	Fe
Tin	Sn
Lead	Pb

Miners — they always have to get their ore in...

This page has four sections with three or four important points in each.
They're all important enough to need learning (except the bit about 1857, etc.).
You need to practise repeating the details from memory. That's the only effective method.

Extracting Iron — the Blast Furnace

Iron is a very common element in the Earth's crust, but good iron ores are only found in a few select places around the world, such as Australia, Canada and Millom.
Iron is extracted from haematite, Fe_2O_3, by reduction (i.e. removal of oxygen) in a blast furnace.
You really do need to know all these details about what goes on in a blast furnace, including the equations.

The Raw Materials are Iron Ore, Coke and Limestone

1) The iron ore contains the iron — which is pretty important.
2) The coke is almost pure carbon. This is for reducing the iron oxide to iron metal.
3) The limestone takes away impurities in the form of slag.

Reducing the Iron Ore to Iron:

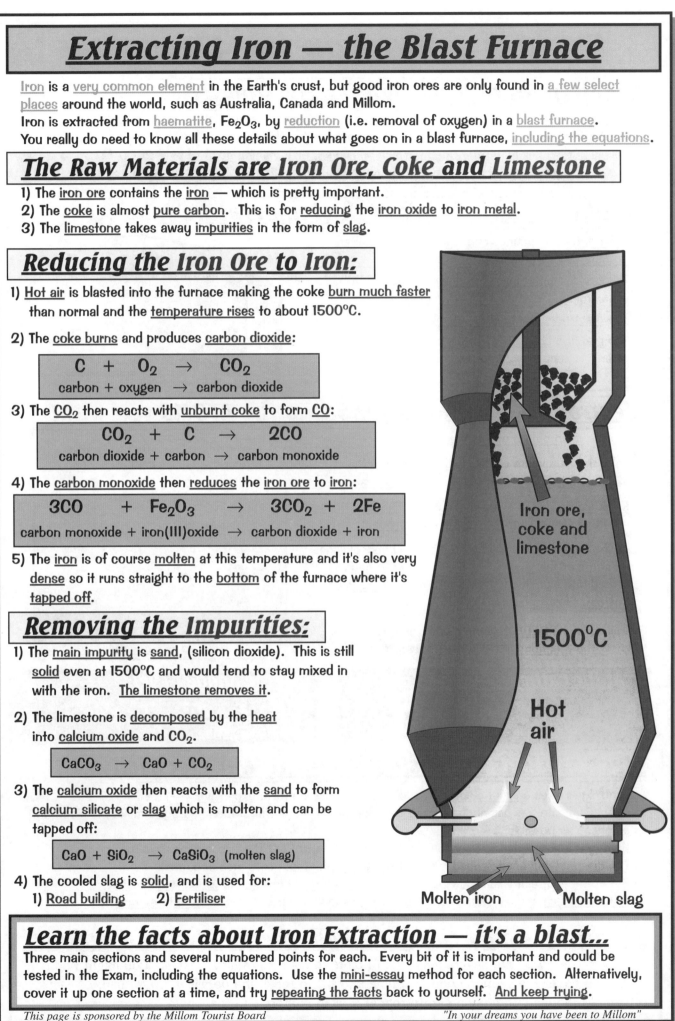

Iron ore, coke and limestone

1500°C

Hot air

Molten iron   Molten slag

1) Hot air is blasted into the furnace making the coke burn much faster than normal and the temperature rises to about 1500°C.

2) The coke burns and produces carbon dioxide:

$$C + O_2 \rightarrow CO_2$$
carbon + oxygen → carbon dioxide

3) The CO_2 then reacts with unburnt coke to form CO:

$$CO_2 + C \rightarrow 2CO$$
carbon dioxide + carbon → carbon monoxide

4) The carbon monoxide then reduces the iron ore to iron:

$$3CO + Fe_2O_3 \rightarrow 3CO_2 + 2Fe$$
carbon monoxide + iron(III)oxide → carbon dioxide + iron

5) The iron is of course molten at this temperature and it's also very dense so it runs straight to the bottom of the furnace where it's tapped off.

Removing the Impurities:

1) The main impurity is sand, (silicon dioxide). This is still solid even at 1500°C and would tend to stay mixed in with the iron. The limestone removes it.

2) The limestone is decomposed by the heat into calcium oxide and CO_2.

$$CaCO_3 \rightarrow CaO + CO_2$$

3) The calcium oxide then reacts with the sand to form calcium silicate or slag which is molten and can be tapped off:

$$CaO + SiO_2 \rightarrow CaSiO_3 \text{ (molten slag)}$$

4) The cooled slag is solid, and is used for:
   1) Road building   2) Fertiliser

Learn the facts about Iron Extraction — it's a blast...

Three main sections and several numbered points for each. Every bit of it is important and could be tested in the Exam, including the equations. Use the mini-essay method for each section. Alternatively, cover it up one section at a time, and try repeating the facts back to yourself. And keep trying.

Extracting Aluminium — Electrolysis

A Molten State is needed for Electrolysis

1) <u>Aluminium</u> is <u>more reactive</u> than <u>carbon</u> so it has to be extracted from its ore by <u>electrolysis</u>.
2) The basic ore is <u>bauxite</u>, and after mining and purifying a <u>white powder</u> is left.
3) This is <u>pure</u> aluminium oxide, Al_2O_3, which has a <u>very high melting point</u> of over 2000°C.
4) For <u>electrolysis</u> to work a <u>molten state</u> is required, and heating to 2000°C would be <u>expensive</u>.

Cryolite is used to lower the temperature (and costs)

1) <u>Instead</u> the aluminium oxide is <u>dissolved</u> in <u>molten cryolite</u> (a less common ore of aluminium).

2) This brings the <u>temperature down</u> to about 900°C, which makes it much <u>cheaper and easier</u>.

3) The <u>electrodes</u> are made of <u>graphite</u> (carbon).

4) The graphite <u>anode</u> (+ve) does need <u>replacing</u> quite often. It keeps <u>reacting</u> to form CO_2.

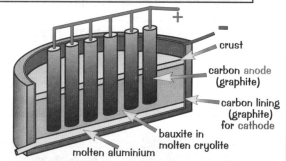

crust
carbon anode (graphite)
carbon lining (graphite) for cathode
bauxite in molten cryolite
molten aluminium

Electrolysis — turning IONS into the ATOMS you want

This is the <u>main object of the exercise</u>:

1) Make the aluminium oxide <u>molten</u> to <u>release</u> the aluminium <u>ions</u>, Al^{3+} so they're <u>free to move</u>.

2) Stick <u>electrodes</u> in — so that the <u>positive</u> Al^{3+} ions will head straight for the <u>negative electrode</u>.

3) At the negative electrode they just can't help picking up some of the <u>spare electrons</u> and "zup", they've turned into aluminium <u>atoms</u> and they <u>sink to the bottom</u>. Pretty clever, I think.

Overall, this is a <u>REDOX reaction</u> and you need to know the <u>reactions</u> at both electrodes:

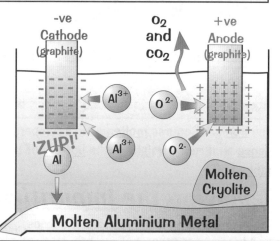

-ve Cathode (graphite)
O_2 and CO_2
+ve Anode (graphite)
Al^{3+}
O^{2-}
'ZUP!'
Al
Al^{3+}
O^{2-}
Molten Cryolite
Molten Aluminium Metal

At the Cathode (–ve):

$$Al^{3+} + 3e^- \rightarrow Al$$

(<u>Reduction</u> — a gain of electrons)

At the Anode (+ve):

$$2O^{2-} \rightarrow O_2 + 4e^-$$

(<u>oxidation</u> — a loss of electrons)

Electrolysis is Expensive — it's all that electricity...

1) Electrolysis uses <u>a lot of electricity</u> and that can make it pretty <u>expensive</u>.
2) Aluminium smelters usually have <u>their own</u> hydro-electric power station <u>nearby</u> to make the electricity as <u>cheap</u> as possible.
3) Energy is also needed to <u>heat</u> the electrolyte mixture to 900°C. This is expensive too.
4) The <u>disappearing anodes</u> need frequent <u>replacement</u>. That costs money as well.
5) But in the end, aluminium now comes out as a <u>reasonably cheap</u> and <u>widely-used</u> metal. <u>A hundred years ago</u> it was a very <u>rare</u> metal, simply because it was so <u>hard to extract</u>.

Electrolysis ain't cheap — well, there's always a charge...

Four main sections with several important points to learn for each. Initially you might find it easiest to cover the sections one at a time and try to <u>recall the details</u> in your head. Ultimately though you should <u>aim to repeat it all in one go</u> with the whole page covered.

Purifying Copper by Electrolysis

1) Aluminium is a <u>very reactive metal</u> and <u>has</u> to be removed from its ore by <u>electrolysis</u>.
2) <u>Copper</u> is a very <u>unreactive</u> metal. Not only is it below carbon in the reactivity series, it's also below <u>hydrogen</u>, which means that copper doesn't even react with <u>water</u>.
3) So copper is obtained <u>very easily</u> from its ore by <u>reduction</u> with <u>carbon</u>.

Very pure copper is needed for electrical conductors

1) The copper produced by <u>reduction</u> <u>isn't pure enough</u> for use in <u>electrical conductors</u>.
2) The <u>purer</u> it is, the better it <u>conducts</u>. <u>Electrolysis</u> is used to obtain <u>very pure copper</u>.

The <u>cathode</u> starts as a <u>thin</u> piece of <u>pure copper</u> and more pure copper <u>adds</u> to it.

Cathode (–ve)

Copper(II) sulphate solution containing $Cu^{2+}_{(aq)}$ ions.

Cu^{2+} Cu^{2+} Cu^{2+} Cu^{2+}

Anode (+ve)

The <u>anode</u> is just a big lump of <u>impure copper</u>, which will <u>dissolve</u>.

Sludge

Pure copper is deposited on the pure cathode (–ve)

The reaction at the <u>cathode</u> is:

$$Cu^{2+}_{(aq)} + 2e^- \rightarrow Cu_{(s)}$$

Copper dissolves from the impure anode (+ve)

The reaction at the <u>anode</u> is:

$$Cu_{(s)} \rightarrow Cu^{2+}_{(aq)} + 2e^-$$

The <u>electrical supply</u> acts by:

1) <u>Pulling electrons off</u> copper atoms at the <u>anode</u> causing them to go into solution as $\underline{Cu^{2+}}$ ions.
2) Then <u>offering electrons</u> at the <u>cathode</u> to nearby $\underline{Cu^{2+}}$ ions to turn them back into <u>copper atoms</u>.
3) The <u>impurities</u> are dropped at the <u>anode</u> as a <u>sludge</u>, whilst <u>pure copper atoms</u> bond to the <u>cathode</u>.
4) The electrolysis can go on for <u>weeks</u> and the cathode is often <u>twenty times bigger</u> at the end of it.

Revision and Electrolysis — they can both go on for weeks...

This is a pretty easy page to learn. The mini-essay method will do you proud here. Don't forget the diagram and the equations. I know it's not much fun, but think how useful all this chemistry will be in your day-to-day life once you've learned it...
    ... hmmm, well... <u>learn it anyway</u>.

Uses of The Three Common Metals

Metals are a lot more interesting than most people ever realise.   (Classic chat-up line No. 71)

Iron is made into steel which is cheap and strong

Iron and steel:

    Advantages: Cheap and strong.

    Disadvantages: Heavy, and prone to rusting away.

Iron and steel are used for:

1) Construction such as bridges and buildings.
2) Cars and lorries and trains and boats and
   NOT PLANES and pushbikes and tanks and pianos...
3) Stainless steel doesn't rust and is used for pans and for fixtures on boats.

Steel may rust and it may not be exactly "space age" but it's strong and it's awful cheap, and it still has a lot of uses. They make cars out of it for one thing... but gone are the halcyon days when car bodies were hand-crafted from ash frames and lovingly honed to perfection. Now they just shovel them out of big presses by the million. Sigh. Mind you there's still the Morgan...

Aluminium is light, strong and corrosion-resistant

Strictly speaking you shouldn't say it's "light", you should say it has "low density".
Whatever. All I know is, it's a lot easier to lift and move around than iron or steel.

Useful Properties:

1) Lightweight.   (OK, *"low density"*. Happy now?)
2) Can be bent and shaped (for making car body panels, etc.)
3) Strong and very rigid when required.
4) Doesn't corrode due to the protective layer of oxide which always quickly covers it.
5) It's also a good conductor of heat and electricity.

Drawbacks: Not as strong as steel and a bit more expensive.

Common uses:

1) Ladders.
2) Aeroplanes.
3) Range Rover body panels (but not the rusty tailgate!).
4) Drink cans — better than tin-plated steel ones which can rust if damaged.
5) Greenhouses and window frames.
6) Big power cables used on pylons.

Copper: good conductor, easily bent and doesn't corrode

This is a winning combination which makes it ideal for:

1) Water pipes and gas pipes, because it can be bent to shape by hand without fracturing.
2) Electrical wiring because it can be easily bent round corners and it conducts really well.
3) Forms useful non corroding alloys such as brass (for trumpets) and bronze (for statues).

Drawbacks: Copper is quite expensive and is not strong.

The Exciting Properties of Metals — learn and enjoy...

Well now, what have we here! Some chemistry which is useful in your everyday life! I reckon it's really pretty helpful if you know the difference between various different metals, although I guess it's only really important if you plan to build your own steam engine or rocket or something. If you don't, then you'll just have to learn it for the Exam and be done with it.

Five Uses Of Limestone

Limestone is a sedimentary rock, formed mainly from sea shells. It is mostly calcium carbonate.

1) Limestone Used as a Building Material

1) It's great for making into blocks for building with. Fine old buildings like cathedrals are often made purely from limestone blocks. Acid rain can be a problem though.
2) It's used for statues and fancy carved bits on nice buildings. But acid rain is even more of a problem.
3) It can just be crushed up into chippings and used for road surfacing.

2) Limestone for Neutralising Acid in lakes and soil

1) Ordinary limestone ground into powder can be used to neutralise acidity in lakes caused by acid rain. It can also be used to neutralise acid soils in fields.
2) It works better and faster if it's turned into slaked lime first:

Turning Limestone into Slaked Lime: first heat it up, then add water

1) The limestone, which is mostly calcium carbonate, is heated and it turns into calcium oxide (CaO):

limestone $\xrightarrow{\text{HEAT}}$ quicklime   or $CaCO_3 \xrightarrow{\text{HEAT}} CaO + CO_2$

2) Calcium oxide reacts violently with water to produce calcium hydroxide (or slaked lime):

quicklime + water $\longrightarrow$ slaked lime   or $CaO + H_2O \longrightarrow Ca(OH)_2$

3) Slaked lime is a white powder and can be applied to fields just like powdered limestone.
4) The advantage is that slaked lime acts much faster at reducing the acidity.

3) Limestone and Clay are Heated to Make Cement

1) Clay contains aluminium and silicates and is dug out of the ground.
2) Powdered clay and powdered limestone are roasted in a rotating kiln to produce a complex mixture of calcium and aluminium silicates, called cement.
3) When cement is mixed with water a slow chemical reaction takes place.
4) This causes the cement to gradually set hard.
5) Cement is usually mixed with sand and chippings to make concrete.
6) Concrete is a very quick and cheap way of constructing buildings — and it shows... — concrete has got to be the most hideously unattractive building material ever known.

4) Glass is made by melting Limestone, Sand and Soda

1) Just heat up limestone (calcium carbonate) with sand (silicon dioxide) and soda (sodium carbonate) until it melts.
2) When the mixture cools it comes out as glass. It's as easy as that. Eat your heart out Mr Pilkington.

5) Limestone dissolves in water to make Limewater

...The old favourite alkaline solution which you can use to test for Carbon Dioxide gas. See page 11.

Tough Revision here — this stuff's rock hard...

Limestone's great for lots of things, but there's a down side — ripping open huge quarries spoils the countryside, especially if the limestone's taken from one of those rare 'limestone pavements' with the special plants and everything. Anyway, learn the whole page till you've got it rock solid...

Making Ammonia: The Haber Process

This is an important industrial process. It produces ammonia (NH_3) which is needed for making fertilisers.

Nitrogen and Hydrogen are needed to make Ammonia

1) The nitrogen is obtained easily from the air, which is 78% nitrogen (and 21% oxygen).
2) The hydrogen is obtained from water (steam) and natural gas (methane, CH_4).
   The methane and steam are reacted together like this:

$$CH_{4\ (g)} + H_2O_{\ (g)} \rightarrow CO_{\ (g)} + 3H_{2\ (g)}$$

3) Hydrogen can also be obtained from crude oil.

The Haber Process is a Reversible Reaction:

$$N_{2\ (g)} + 3H_{2\ (g)} \rightleftharpoons 2NH_{3\ (g)} \quad (+ \text{ heat})$$

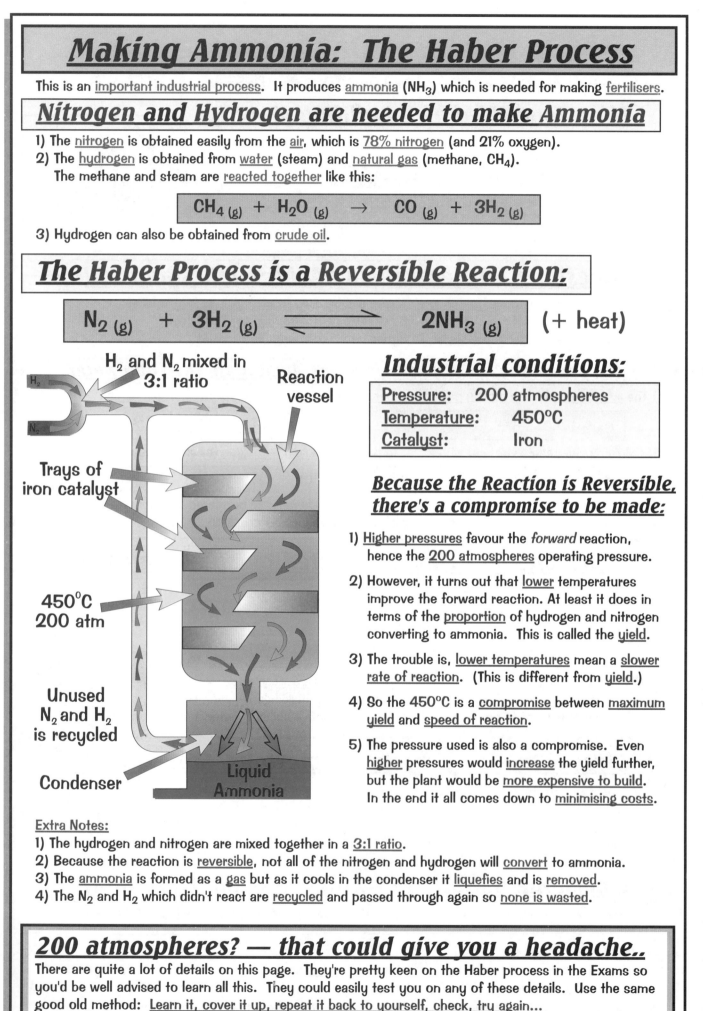

H₂ and N₂ mixed in 3:1 ratio

Reaction vessel

Trays of iron catalyst

450°C 200 atm

Unused N_2 and H_2 is recycled

Condenser

Liquid Ammonia

Industrial conditions:

Pressure:	200 atmospheres
Temperature:	450°C
Catalyst:	Iron

Because the Reaction is Reversible, there's a compromise to be made:

1) Higher pressures favour the *forward* reaction, hence the 200 atmospheres operating pressure.

2) However, it turns out that lower temperatures improve the forward reaction. At least it does in terms of the proportion of hydrogen and nitrogen converting to ammonia. This is called the yield.

3) The trouble is, lower temperatures mean a slower rate of reaction. (This is different from yield.)

4) So the 450°C is a compromise between maximum yield and speed of reaction.

5) The pressure used is also a compromise. Even higher pressures would increase the yield further, but the plant would be more expensive to build. In the end it all comes down to minimising costs.

Extra Notes:
1) The hydrogen and nitrogen are mixed together in a 3:1 ratio.
2) Because the reaction is reversible, not all of the nitrogen and hydrogen will convert to ammonia.
3) The ammonia is formed as a gas but as it cools in the condenser it liquefies and is removed.
4) The N_2 and H_2 which didn't react are recycled and passed through again so none is wasted.

200 atmospheres? — that could give you a headache..

There are quite a lot of details on this page. They're pretty keen on the Haber process in the Exams so you'd be well advised to learn all this. They could easily test you on any of these details. Use the same good old method: Learn it, cover it up, repeat it back to yourself, check, try again...

Using Ammonia to Make Fertilisers

On this page are two reactions involving ammonia that you need to be familiar with. Somehow, I don't think I'd have either of them in my list of "Top Ten Most Riveting Chemistry Topics":

1) Ammonia Can be Oxidised To Form Nitric Acid

There are two stages to this reaction:

a) Ammonia gas reacts with oxygen over a hot platinum catalyst:

$$4NH_{3\,(g)} + 5O_{2\,(g)} \rightarrow 4NO_{(g)} + 6H_2O_{(g)}$$

This first stage is very exothermic and produces its own heat to keep it going.
The nitrogen monoxide must be cooled before the next stage, which happens easily:

b) The nitrogen monoxide reacts with water and oxygen...

$$6NO_{(g)} + 3O_{2\,(g)} + 2H_2O_{(g)} \rightarrow 4HNO_{3\,(g)} + 2NO_{(g)}$$

...to form nitric acid, HNO_3

Gripping stuff. Anyway, the nitric acid produced is very useful for other chemical processes.
One such use is to make ammonium nitrate fertiliser...

2) Ammonia can be neutralised with Nitric Acid...

...to make Ammonium Nitrate fertiliser

This is a straightforward and spectacularly unexciting neutralisation reaction between an alkali (ammonia) and an acid. The result is of course a neutral salt: *(prod me if I fall asleep)*

$$NH_{3\,(g)} + HNO_{3\,(aq)} \rightarrow NH_4NO_{3\,(aq)}$$
Ammonia + Nitric acid   →   Ammonium nitrate

Ammonium nitrate is an especially good fertiliser because it has nitrogen from two sources, the ammonia and the nitric acid. Kind of a double dose. Plants need nitrogen to make proteins.

Excessive Nitrate Fertiliser causes Eutrophication and Health Problems

1) If nitrate fertilisers wash into streams they set off a cycle of mega-growth, mega-death and mega-decay. Plants and green algae grow out of control, then start to die off because there's too many of them, then bacteria take over, feeding off the dying plants and using up all the oxygen in the water. Then the fish all die because they can't get enough oxygen. Lovely.
It's called eutrophication (See the Biology Book for more details). It's all good clean fun.

2) If too many nitrates get into drinking water it can cause health problems, especially for young babies. Nitrates prevent the blood from carrying oxygen properly and children can turn blue and even die.

3) To avoid these problems it's important that artificial nitrate fertilisers are applied carefully by all farmers — they must take care not to apply too much, and not if it's going to rain soon.

There's nowt wrong wi' just spreadin' muck on it...

Basically, this page is about how ammonia is turned into ammonium nitrate fertiliser. Alas there are some seriously tedious details which they seem to expect you to learn. Don't ask me why. Anyway, the more you learn, the more you know. (He said, wisely and meaninglessly.)

Revision Summary for Section Two

Section Two is pretty interesting stuff I reckon. Relatively speaking. Anyway, whether it is or it isn't, the only thing that really matters is whether you've learnt it all or not. These questions aren't exactly friendly, but they're a seriously serious way of finding out what you don't know. And don't forget, that's what revision is all about — finding out what you don't know and then learning it till you do. Practise these questions as often as necessary — not just once. Your ultimate aim is to be able to answer all of them easily.

1) Describe how crude oil is formed. What length of time did it take?
2) What does crude oil consist of?
3) Draw the full diagram of fractional distillation of crude oil.
4) What are the seven main fractions obtained from crude oil, and what are they used for?
5) What are hydrocarbons? Describe four properties and how they vary with the molecule size.
6) Give the equations for complete and incomplete combustion of hydrocarbons.
7) Which type is dangerous and why? What are the flames for these two types of combustion?
8) What is "cracking"? Why is it done?
9) Give a typical example of a substance which is cracked and the products that you get.
10) What are the industrial conditions used for cracking?
11) What are alkanes and alkenes? What is the basic difference between them?
12) Draw the structures of the first four alkanes and the first three alkenes and give their names.
13) List four differences in the chemical properties of alkanes and alkenes.
14) What are polymers? What kind of substances can form polymers?
15) Draw diagrams to show how ethene, propene and styrene form polymers.
16) Name four types of plastic, give their physical properties and say what they're used for.
17) What are rocks, ores and minerals? Which metal is found as a metal rather than an ore?
18) What are the two methods for extracting metals from their ores?
19) What decides which method is needed?
20) Draw a diagram of a blast furnace. What are the three raw materials used in it?
21) Write down the equations for how iron is obtained from its ore in the blast furnace.
22) What is slag? Write two equations for the formation of slag, and give two uses of it.
23) How is aluminium extracted from its ore? Give four operational details and draw a diagram.
24) Explain how aluminium metal is obtained from the process, and give the two equations.
25) Explain three reasons why this process is so expensive.
26) How is copper extracted from its ore? How is it then purified, and why does it need to be?
27) Draw a diagram for the purifying process and give the two equations.
28) Describe how the pure copper is obtained.
29) Describe the plus and minus points of iron (and steel), and give six uses for it.
30) Describe the plus and minus points of aluminium, and give six uses for it.
31) Describe the plus and minus points of copper, and give three uses for it.
32) What are the five main uses of limestone?
33) Give the equations for turning limestone into slaked lime. Why do we bother?
34) Give four details about what cement is made of and how it works.
35) What is the Haber process? What are the raw materials for it and how are they obtained?
36) Draw a full diagram for the Haber process and explain the temperature and pressure used.
37) Give full details of how ammonia is turned into nitric acid, including equations.
38) What is the main use of ammonia? Give the equation for producing ammonium nitrate.
39) Give two problems resulting from nitrate fertilisers. Explain fully what "eutrophication" is.

Nine Types of Chemical Change

There are <u>nine</u> types of chemical change you should know about. It's well worth learning exactly what each of them is, <u>here and now</u>, rather than living the rest of your life in a confused haze.

1) THERMAL DECOMPOSITION — *breakdown on heating*

This is when a substance <u>breaks down</u> into simpler substances <u>when heated</u>, often with the help of a <u>catalyst</u>. It's different from a reaction because there's only <u>one substance</u> to start with. <u>Cracking of hydrocarbons</u> is a good example of thermal decomposition.

2) NEUTRALISATION — *acid + alkali gives salt + water*

This is simply when an <u>acid</u> reacts with an <u>alkali</u> (or base) to form a <u>neutral</u> product, which is neither acid nor alkali (usually a <u>salt</u> solution).

3) DISPLACEMENT — *one metal kicking another one out*

This is a reaction where a <u>more reactive</u> element reacts with a compound and <u>pushes out</u> a <u>less reactive</u> "rival" element. <u>Metals</u> are the most common example. Magnesium will react with iron sulphate to push the iron out and form magnesium sulphate.

4) PRECIPITATION — *solid forms in solution*

This is a reaction where <u>two solutions react</u> and a <u>solid</u> forms in the solution and <u>sinks</u>. The solid is said to "<u>precipitate out</u>" and, confusingly, the solid is also called "<u>a precipitate</u>".

5) OXIDATION — *loss of electrons*

<u>Oxidation</u> is the <u>addition of oxygen</u>. Iron becoming iron oxide is oxidation. The more technical and general definition of oxidation is "<u>the loss of electrons</u>".

Remember
"OIL RIG"
(Oxidation Is Loss, Reduction Is Gain)

6) REDUCTION — *gain of electrons*

<u>Reduction</u> is the <u>reverse of oxidation</u>, i.e. the <u>loss of oxygen</u>. Iron oxide is <u>reduced</u> to iron. The more technical and general definition of reduction is "<u>the gain of electrons</u>". Note that <u>reduction</u> is <u>gain</u> of electrons. That's the way to remember it — it's kinda <u>the wrong way round</u>.

7) EXOTHERMIC REACTIONS — *give out heat*

<u>Exothermic</u> reactions <u>give out energy</u>, usually as heat. "Exo-" as in "Exit", or "out". Any time a <u>fuel burns</u> and <u>gives off heat</u> it's an <u>exothermic</u> reaction.

8) ENDOTHERMIC REACTIONS — *take in heat*

<u>Endothermic</u> reactions need heat <u>putting in</u> constantly to make them work. Heat is needed to <u>form chemical bonds</u>. The <u>products</u> of endothermic reactions are likely to be <u>more useful</u> than the <u>reactants</u>, otherwise we <u>wouldn't bother putting all the energy in</u>, e.g. turning <u>iron oxide</u> into <u>iron</u> is an endothermic process. We need a lot of heat from the coke to keep it happening.

9) REVERSIBLE REACTIONS — *they go both ways*

<u>Reversible</u> reactions are ones that will cheerfully go in <u>both</u> directions at the <u>same time</u>. In other words, the <u>products</u> can easily turn back into the <u>original reactants</u>.

Nine more fantastic chat-up lines just waiting to happen...

<u>A nice easy page to learn</u>. You should know a lot of this already.
Anyway, cover the page and expose each yellow box (*without* the other bit of the heading!) one by one and try to explain it to yourself before uncovering the text to check.

Balancing Equations

Equations need a lot of practice if you're going to get them right.
This is just a reminder of the basics.
But every time you do an equation you need to practise getting it right rather than skating over it.

The Symbol Equation shows the atoms on both sides:

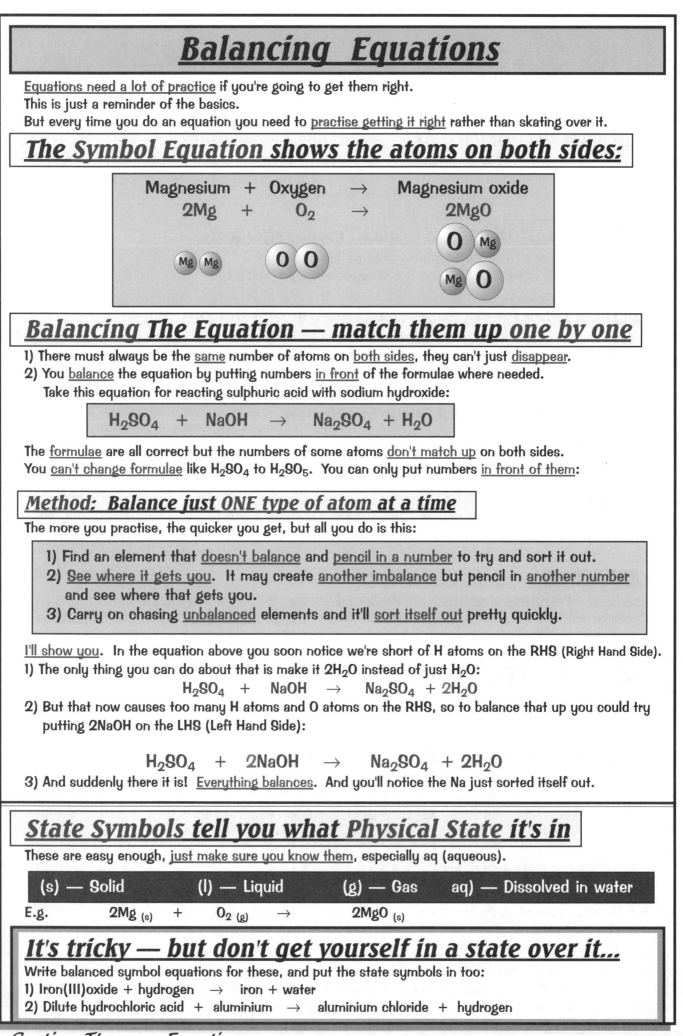

Magnesium + Oxygen → Magnesium oxide
2Mg + O_2 → 2MgO

Balancing The Equation — match them up one by one

1) There must always be the same number of atoms on both sides, they can't just disappear.
2) You balance the equation by putting numbers in front of the formulae where needed.

Take this equation for reacting sulphuric acid with sodium hydroxide:

$$H_2SO_4 + NaOH \rightarrow Na_2SO_4 + H_2O$$

The formulae are all correct but the numbers of some atoms don't match up on both sides.
You can't change formulae like H_2SO_4 to H_2SO_5. You can only put numbers in front of them:

Method: Balance just ONE type of atom at a time

The more you practise, the quicker you get, but all you do is this:

> 1) Find an element that doesn't balance and pencil in a number to try and sort it out.
> 2) See where it gets you. It may create another imbalance but pencil in another number and see where that gets you.
> 3) Carry on chasing unbalanced elements and it'll sort itself out pretty quickly.

I'll show you. In the equation above you soon notice we're short of H atoms on the RHS (Right Hand Side).
1) The only thing you can do about that is make it $2H_2O$ instead of just H_2O:

$$H_2SO_4 + NaOH \rightarrow Na_2SO_4 + 2H_2O$$

2) But that now causes too many H atoms and O atoms on the RHS, so to balance that up you could try putting 2NaOH on the LHS (Left Hand Side):

$$H_2SO_4 + 2NaOH \rightarrow Na_2SO_4 + 2H_2O$$

3) And suddenly there it is! Everything balances. And you'll notice the Na just sorted itself out.

State Symbols tell you what Physical State it's in

These are easy enough, just make sure you know them, especially aq (aqueous).

(s) — Solid	(l) — Liquid	(g) — Gas	aq) — Dissolved in water

E.g. $2Mg_{(s)}$ + $O_{2(g)}$ → $2MgO_{(s)}$

It's tricky — but don't get yourself in a state over it...

Write balanced symbol equations for these, and put the state symbols in too:
1) Iron(III)oxide + hydrogen → iron + water
2) Dilute hydrochloric acid + aluminium → aluminium chloride + hydrogen

Electrolysis and The Half Equations

(Another psychedelic sixties pop group? Sigh... if only.)

Electrolysis means "Splitting Up with Electricity"

1) It requires a liquid, called the <u>electrolyte</u> which will <u>conduct electricity</u>.
2) Electrolytes are usually <u>free ions dissolved in water</u>,
   e.g. <u>dilute acids</u> like HCl, and <u>dissolved salts</u>, e.g. NaCl solution.
3) Electrolytes can also be <u>molten ionic substances</u>, but this involves <u>higher</u>
   <u>temperatures</u>. In either case it's the <u>free ions</u> which <u>conduct</u> the electricity
   and allow the whole thing to work.
4) The electrical supply acts like an <u>electron pump</u>, taking electrons <u>away</u>
   <u>from</u> the <u>+ve anode</u> and <u>onto the –ve cathode</u>. Ions <u>gain or lose</u> electrons
   at the electrodes and <u>neutral atoms and molecules</u> are released.

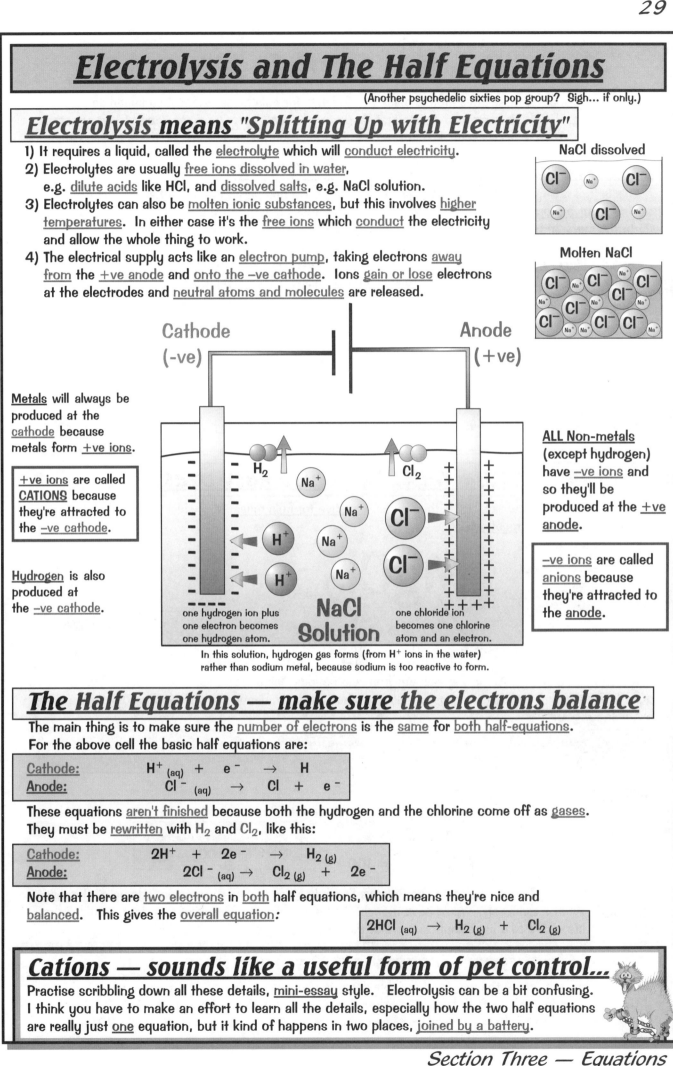

<u>Metals</u> will always be
produced at the
<u>cathode</u> because
metals form <u>+ve ions</u>.

+ve ions are called
CATIONS because
they're attracted to
the –ve cathode.

<u>Hydrogen</u> is also
produced at
the <u>–ve cathode</u>.

<u>ALL Non-metals</u>
(except hydrogen)
have <u>–ve ions</u> and
so they'll be
produced at the <u>+ve</u>
<u>anode</u>.

–ve ions are called
anions because
they're attracted to
the anode.

Cathode (-ve)   Anode (+ve)

one hydrogen ion plus
one electron becomes
one hydrogen atom.

NaCl Solution

one chloride ion
becomes one chlorine
atom and an electron.

In this solution, hydrogen gas forms (from H^+ ions in the water)
rather than sodium metal, because sodium is too reactive to form.

The Half Equations — make sure the electrons balance

The main thing is to make sure the <u>number of electrons</u> is the <u>same</u> for <u>both half-equations</u>.
For the above cell the basic half equations are:

<u>Cathode:</u> $H^+_{(aq)} + e^- \rightarrow H$
<u>Anode:</u> $Cl^-_{(aq)} \rightarrow Cl + e^-$

These equations <u>aren't finished</u> because both the hydrogen and the chlorine come off as <u>gases</u>.
They must be <u>rewritten</u> with H_2 and Cl_2, like this:

<u>Cathode:</u> $2H^+ + 2e^- \rightarrow H_{2 (g)}$
<u>Anode:</u> $2Cl^-_{(aq)} \rightarrow Cl_{2 (g)} + 2e^-$

Note that there are <u>two electrons</u> in <u>both</u> half equations, which means they're nice and
<u>balanced</u>. This gives the <u>overall equation</u>:

$$2HCl_{(aq)} \rightarrow H_{2 (g)} + Cl_{2 (g)}$$

Cations — sounds like a useful form of pet control...

Practise scribbling down all these details, <u>mini-essay</u> style. Electrolysis can be a bit confusing.
I think you have to make an effort to learn all the details, especially how the two half equations
are really just <u>one</u> equation, but it kind of happens in two places, <u>joined by a battery</u>.

Relative Formula Mass

The biggest trouble with Relative atomic mass and Relative formula mass is that they sound so bloodcurdling. *"With big scary names like that they must be really, really complicated."* I hear you cry. Nope, wrong. They're dead easy. Take a few deep breaths, and just enjoy, as the mists slowly clear...

Relative Atomic Mass, A_r — easy peasy

1) This is just a way of saying how heavy different atoms are compared to each other.
2) The relative atomic mass A_r is nothing more than the mass number of the element.
3) In the periodic table, the elements all have two numbers. The smaller one is the atomic number (how many protons it has).
   But the bigger one is the mass number (how many protons and neutrons it has) which, kind of obviously, is also the relative atomic mass.   Easy peasy, I'd say.

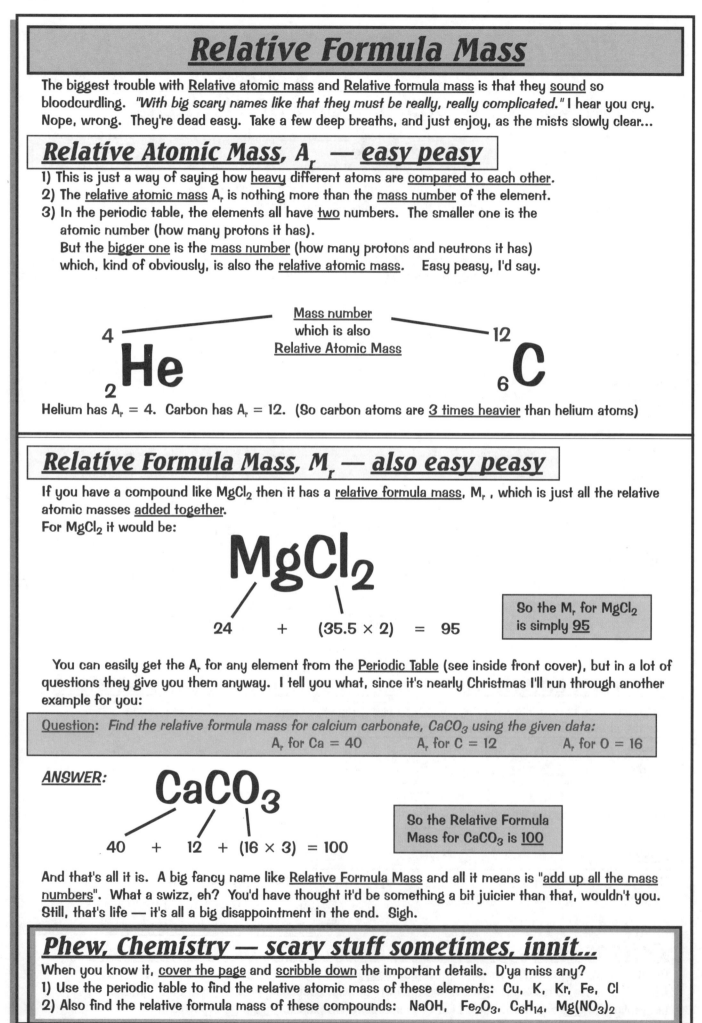

Helium has A_r = 4. Carbon has A_r = 12. (So carbon atoms are 3 times heavier than helium atoms)

Relative Formula Mass, M_r — also easy peasy

If you have a compound like $MgCl_2$ then it has a relative formula mass, M_r , which is just all the relative atomic masses added together.

For $MgCl_2$ it would be:

$$MgCl_2$$

24   +   (35.5 × 2)   =   95

So the M_r for $MgCl_2$ is simply 95

   You can easily get the A_r for any element from the Periodic Table (see inside front cover), but in a lot of questions they give you them anyway. I tell you what, since it's nearly Christmas I'll run through another example for you:

Question: *Find the relative formula mass for calcium carbonate, $CaCO_3$ using the given data:*
                 A_r for Ca = 40 A_r for C = 12 A_r for O = 16

ANSWER: $CaCO_3$

   40   +   12   + (16 × 3) = 100

So the Relative Formula Mass for $CaCO_3$ is 100

And that's all it is. A big fancy name like Relative Formula Mass and all it means is "add up all the mass numbers". What a swizz, eh? You'd have thought it'd be something a bit juicier than that, wouldn't you. Still, that's life — it's all a big disappointment in the end. Sigh.

Phew, Chemistry — scary stuff sometimes, innit...

When you know it, cover the page and scribble down the important details. D'ya miss any?
1) Use the periodic table to find the relative atomic mass of these elements: Cu, K, Kr, Fe, Cl
2) Also find the relative formula mass of these compounds: NaOH, Fe_2O_3, C_6H_{14}, $Mg(NO_3)_2$

Two Formula Mass Calculations

Although Relative Atomic Mass and Relative Formula Mass are <u>easy enough</u>, it can get just a tadge <u>trickier</u> when you start getting into other calculations which use them. It depends on how good your maths is basically, because it's all to do with ratios and percentages.

Calculating % Mass of an Element in a Compound

This is actually dead easy — so long as you've learnt this formula:

$$\text{PERCENTAGE MASS OF AN ELEMENT IN A COMPOUND} = \frac{A_r \times \text{No. of atoms (of that element)}}{M_r \text{ (of whole compound)}} \times 100$$

If you don't learn the formula then you'd better be pretty smart — or you'll struggle.

<u>EXAMPLE:</u> *Find the percentage mass of sodium in sodium carbonate, Na_2CO_3*
<u>ANSWER:</u>
  A_r of sodium = 23, A_r of carbon = 12, A_r of oxygen = 16
  M_r of Na_2CO_3 = $(2 \times 23) + 12 + (3 \times 16) = 106$

Now use the formula: $\underline{\text{Percentage mass}} = \dfrac{A_r \times n}{M_r} \times 100 = \dfrac{23 \times 2}{106} \times 100 = 43.4\%$

And there you have it. Sodium represents <u>43.4%</u> of the mass of sodium carbonate.

Finding The Empirical Formula (from Masses or Percentages)

This also sounds a lot worse than it really is. Try this for an easy peasy <u>stepwise method</u>:

1) <u>List all the elements</u> in the compound (there's usually only two or three!)
2) <u>Underneath them</u>, write their <u>experimental masses or percentages</u>.
3) <u>Divide</u> each mass or percentage <u>by the A_r</u> for that particular element.
4) Turn the numbers you get into <u>a nice simple ratio</u>
   by multiplying and/or dividing them by well-chosen numbers.
5) Get the ratio in its <u>simplest form</u>, and that tells you the formula of the compound.

<u>EXAMPLE:</u> *Find the empirical formula of the iron oxide produced when 44.8g of iron react with 19.2g of oxygen. (A_r for iron = 56, A_r for oxygen =16)*
<u>METHOD:</u>

	Fe	O
1) List the two elements:	Fe	O
2) Write in the experimental masses:	44.8	19.2
3) Divide by the A_r for each element:	$44.8/56 = 0.8$	$19.2/16 = 1.2$
4) Multiply by 10...	8	12
...then divide by 4:	2	3

5) So the simplest formula is 2 atoms of Fe to 3 atoms of O, i.e. Fe_2O_3. And that's it done.

> *You need to realise (for the Exam) that this <u>EMPIRICAL METHOD</u> (i.e. based on <u>experiment</u>) is the <u>only way</u> of finding out the formula of a compound. Rust is iron oxide, sure, but is it FeO, or Fe_2O_3? Only an experiment to determine the empirical formula will tell you for certain.*

Old Dmitri Mendeleyev did this sort of stuff in his sleep — the old rogue...

Make sure you <u>learn the formula</u> at the top and the five rules in the red box. Then try these:
1) Find the percentage mass of oxygen in these: a) Fe_2O_3 b) H_2O c) $CaCO_3$ d) H_2SO_4
2) Find the empirical formula when 2.4g of carbon reacts with 0.8g of hydrogen.

Calculating Masses in Reactions

These can be kinda scary too, but chill out, little white-faced one — just relax and enjoy.

The Three Important Steps — not to be missed...

(Miss one out and it'll all go horribly wrong, believe me)

1) Write out the balanced Equation
2) Work out M_r — just for the two bits you want
3) Apply the rule: Divide to get one, then multiply to get all
(But you have to apply this first to the substance they give information about, and then the other one!)

EXAMPLE: What mass of magnesium oxide is produced when 60g of magnesium is burned in air?

ANSWER:

1) Write out the balanced equation:

$$2Mg + O_2 \rightarrow 2MgO$$

2) Work out the Relative Formula masses:

(don't do the oxygen — we don't need it)

$$2 \times 24 \rightarrow 2 \times (24+16)$$
$$48 \rightarrow 80$$

3) Apply the rule: Divide to get one, then multiply to get all

The two numbers, 48 and 80, tell us that   48g of Mg react to give 80g of MgO.
Here's the tricky bit. You've now got to be able to write this down:

48g of Mg ......reacts to give.....80g of MgO

1g of Mg ......reacts to give.....

60g of Mg .....reacts to give......

The big clue is that in the question they've said we want to burn "60g of magnesium"
i.e. they've told us how much magnesium to have, and that's how you know to write down the left hand side of it first, because:

We'll first need to ÷ by 48 to get 1g of Mg
and then need to × by 60 to get 60g of Mg.

Then you can work out the numbers on the other side (shown in orange below) by realising that you must divide both sides by 48 and then multiply both sides by 60. It's tricky.

÷48   48g of Mg .... 80g of MgO   ÷48
      1g of Mg .... 1.67g of MgO
×60   60g of Mg .... 100g of MgO   ×60

You should realise that in practice 100% yield may not be obtained in some reactions, so the amount of product might be slightly less than calculated.

This finally tells us that 60g of magnesium will produce 100g of magnesium oxide.
If the question had said "Find how much magnesium gives 500g of magnesium oxide.", you'd fill in the MgO side first instead, because that's the one you'd have the information about. Got it? Good-O!

Reaction Mass Calculations? — no worries, matey...

Learn the three rules in the red box and practise the example till you can do it fluently.
1) Find the mass of calcium which gives 30g of calcium oxide (CaO), when burnt in air.

Calculating Volumes

These are OK as long as you LEARN the formula in the red box and know how to use it.

1) Calculating the Volume When you know the Masses

For this type of question there are two stages:
1) Find the reacting mass, exactly like in the examples on the last page.
2) Then convert the mass into a volume using this formula:

$$\frac{\text{VOL. OF GAS (in cm}^3)}{24,000} = \frac{\text{MASS OF GAS}}{M_r \text{ of gas}}$$

This formula comes from the well known(!) fact that:

A mass of M_r, in grams, of any gas, will always occupy 24 litres
(at room temperature and pressure) — and it's the same for any gas.

I reckon it's easier to learn and use the formula, but it's certainly worth knowing that fact too.

EXAMPLE: Find the volume of carbon dioxide produced (at room T and P) when 2.7g of carbon is completely burned in oxygen. (A_r of carbon = 12, A_r of oxygen = 16)
ANSWER:

1) Balanced equation:
2) Fill in M_r for each:
3) Divide for one, times for all:

$$C \ + \ O_2 \ \rightarrow \ CO_2$$

$\div 12$ (12   32   44) $\div 12$
    1 .... 3.6666667
$\times 2.7$ 2.7 .... 9.8999999) $\times 2.7$

4) So 2.7g of C gives 9.9g of CO_2.   = 9.9
     Now the new bit:
5) Using the above formula:

$$\frac{\text{Volume}}{24,000} = \frac{\text{MASS}}{M_r} \Rightarrow \text{Volume} = \frac{\text{MASS} \times 24,000}{M_r}$$

so Volume = (MASS/M_r) × 24,000 = (9.9/44) × 24000 = 5400.

= 5400cm^3 or 5.40 litres

---

2) Calculating the Mass when you're given the Volume

For this type of question the two stages are in the reverse order:
1) First find the mass from the volume using the same formula as before:

$$\frac{\text{Vol. of gas (in cm}^3)}{24,000} = \frac{\text{MASS OF GAS}}{M_r \text{ of gas}}$$

2) Then find the reacting mass, exactly like in the examples on the last page.

EXAMPLE: Find the mass of 6.2 litres of oxygen gas. (A_r of oxygen = 16)

ANSWER: Using the above formula: $\frac{6,200}{24,000} = \frac{\text{Mass of Gas}}{32}$

(Look out, 32, because it's O_2)

Hence, Mass of Gas = (6,200/24,000) × 32 = 8.2666667 = 8.27g

The question would likely go on to ask what mass of CO_2 would be produced if this much oxygen reacted with carbon. In that case you would now just apply the same old method from the previous page (as used above).

Calculating Volumes — it's just a gas...

Make sure you learn the formula in the red box at the top and that you know how to use it.
1) Find the volume of 2.5g of methane gas, CH_4, (at room T & P).
2) Find the mass of oxide (MgO) produced when magnesium is burned with 1.7 litres of oxygen.

Electrolysis Calculations

The important bit here is to get the balanced half equations, because they determine <u>the relative amounts</u> of the two substances produced at the two electrodes. After that it's all the same as before, working out masses using M_r values, and volumes using the "$M_r(g) = 24$ litres" rule.

The Three Steps for Electrolysis Calculations

1) Write down the <u>two balanced half equations</u>
   (i.e. match the number of electrons)
2) Write down the <u>balanced formulae</u> for the
   two products obtained from the two electrodes.
3) <u>Write in the M_r values</u> underneath each
   and carry on as for previous calculations.

<u>EXAMPLE</u>: In the electrolysis of sodium chloride, hydrogen gas is released at the cathode and chlorine gas is released at the anode. If 0.25g of hydrogen gas are collected at the cathode, find the volume of chlorine released.

<u>ANSWER:</u>

1) Balanced <u>half equations</u>:

$$2H^+ + 2e \rightarrow H_2$$
$$2Cl^- - 2e^- \rightarrow Cl_2$$

(2×1 because it's H_2 not just H)

2) <u>Balanced formulae of products:</u>
   (as obtained from the balanced half equations)

(2×35.5 because it's Cl_2 not just Cl)

3) <u>Write in M_r values:</u>
   ...and carry on as usual

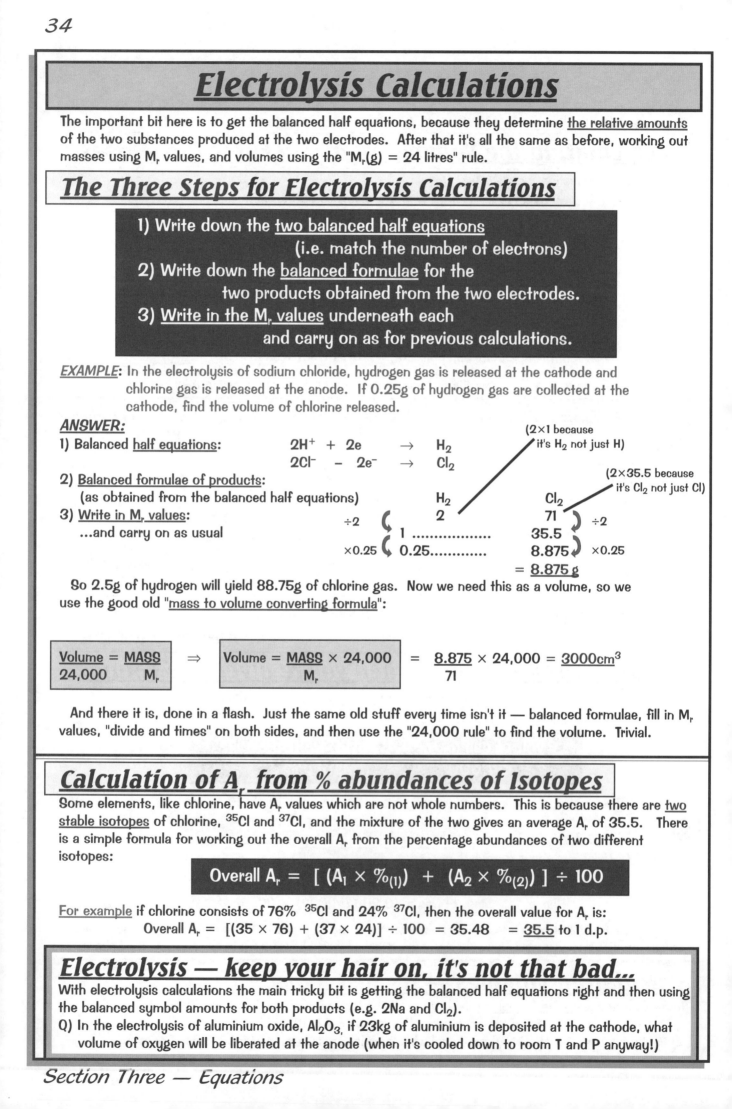

	H_2	Cl_2	
÷2	2	71	÷2
	1	35.5	
×0.25	0.25.............	8.875	×0.25
		= <u>8.875 g</u>	

So 2.5g of hydrogen will yield 88.75g of chlorine gas. Now we need this as a volume, so we use the good old "<u>mass to volume converting formula</u>":

$$\text{Volume} = \frac{\text{MASS}}{24,000} M_r \Rightarrow \text{Volume} = \frac{\text{MASS} \times 24,000}{M_r} = \frac{8.875 \times 24,000}{71} = \underline{3000cm^3}$$

And there it is, done in a flash. Just the same old stuff every time isn't it — balanced formulae, fill in M_r values, "divide and times" on both sides, and then use the "24,000 rule" to find the volume. Trivial.

Calculation of A_r from % abundances of Isotopes

Some elements, like chlorine, have A_r values which are not whole numbers. This is because there are <u>two stable isotopes</u> of chlorine, ^{35}Cl and ^{37}Cl, and the mixture of the two gives an average A_r of 35.5. There is a simple formula for working out the overall A_r from the percentage abundances of two different isotopes:

$$\text{Overall } A_r = [(A_1 \times \%_{(1)}) + (A_2 \times \%_{(2)})] \div 100$$

<u>For example</u> if chlorine consists of 76% ^{35}Cl and 24% ^{37}Cl, then the overall value for A_r is:
$$\text{Overall } A_r = [(35 \times 76) + (37 \times 24)] \div 100 = 35.48 = \underline{35.5} \text{ to 1 d.p.}$$

Electrolysis — keep your hair on, it's not that bad...

With electrolysis calculations the main tricky bit is getting the balanced half equations right and then using the balanced symbol amounts for both products (e.g. 2Na and Cl_2).

Q) In the electrolysis of aluminium oxide, Al_2O_3, if 23kg of aluminium is deposited at the cathode, what volume of oxygen will be liberated at the anode (when it's cooled down to room T and P anyway!)

The Mole

The Mole is really confusing. I think it's the word that puts people off. It's very difficult to see the relevance of the word "mole" to different-sized piles of brightly-coloured powders.

"THE MOLE" is simply the name given to a certain number

Just like "a million" is this many: 1 000 000; or "a billion" is this many: 1 000 000 000, so "a mole" is this many: 602 300 000 000 000 000 000 000   or 6.023×10^{23}.

1) And that's all it is. Just a number. The burning question, of course, is why is it such a silly long one like that, and with a six at the front?

2) The answer is that when you get precisely that number of atoms or molecules, of any element or compound, then, conveniently, they weigh exactly the same number of grams as the Relative Atomic Mass, A_r (or M_r) of the element or compound.
   This is arranged on purpose of course, to make things easier.

> One mole of atoms or molecules of any substance will have a mass in grams equal to the Relative Formula Mass (A_r or M_r) for that substance.

EXAMPLES:

Carbon has an A_r of 12.   So one mole of carbon weighs exactly 12g
Iron has an A_r of 56.   So one mole of iron weighs exactly 56g
Nitrogen gas, N_2, has an M_r of 28 (2×14).   So one mole of N_2 weighs exactly 28g
Carbon dioxide, CO_2, has an M_r of 44.   So one mole of CO_2 weighs exactly 44g

This means that 12g of carbon, or 56g of iron, or 28g of N_2, or 44g of CO_2, all contain the same number of atoms, namely one mole or 6×10^{23} atoms or molecules.

Nice Easy Formula for finding the Number of Moles in a given mass:

> NUMBER OF MOLES   = Mass in g   (of element or compound)
> M_r (of element or compound)

EXAMPLE: How many moles are there in 42g of carbon?
ANSWER: No. of moles   = Mass (g) / M_r = 42/12   = 3.5 moles   Easy Peasy

"Relative Formula Mass" is also "Molar Mass"

1) We've been very happy using the Relative Formula Mass, M_r all through the calculations.
2) In fact, that was already using the idea of Moles because M_r is actually the mass of one mole in g, or as we sometimes call it, the molar mass.
3) It follows that the volume of one mole of any gas will be 24 litres — the molar volume.

A "One Molar Solution" Contains "One Mole per Litre"

This is pretty easy. So a 2M solution of NaOH contains 2 moles of NaOH per litre of solution.
You need to know how many moles there'll be in a given volume:

> NUMBER OF MOLES   = Volume in Litres $\times$ Molarity of solution

EXAMPLE: How many moles in 185cm^3 of a 2M solution?   ANS: $0.185 \times 2 = 0.37$ moles

Moles — a suitably silly name for such a confusing idea...

It's possible to do all the calculations on the previous pages without ever talking about moles. You just concentrate on M_r and A_r all the time instead. In fact M_r and A_r represent moles anyway, but I think it's less confusing if moles aren't mentioned at all. Ask "Teach" how much of this page you should learn.

Revision Summary for Section Three

Some more horrid questions to stress you out. The thing is though, why bother doing easy questions? These meaty monsters find out what you really know, and worse, what you really don't. Yeah, I know, it's kinda scary, but if you want to get anywhere in life you've got to face up to a bit of hardship. That's just the way it is. Take a few deep breaths and then try these:

(Answers on P. 80)

1) Describe each of these nine types of chemical change: Thermal decomposition, neutralisation, displacement, precipitation, oxidation, reduction, exothermic, endothermic, reversible.
2) Give three rules for balancing equations. Balance these and put the state symbols in:
   a) $CaCO_3 + HCl \rightarrow CaCl_2 + H_2O + CO_2$
   b) $Ca + H_2O \rightarrow Ca(OH)_2 + H_2$
   c) $H_2SO_4 + KOH \rightarrow K_2SO_4 + H_2O$
   d) $Fe_2O_3 + H_2 \rightarrow Fe + H_2O$
   e) propane + oxygen $\rightarrow$ carbon dioxide + water
3) What is electrolysis? What is needed for electrolysis to take place?
4) Draw a diagram showing the electrolysis of NaCl solution. What are cations and anions?
5) What is the rule for balancing half equations?
6) What are A_r and M_r?
7) What is the relationship between A_r and the number of protons and neutrons in the atom?
8) Find A_r or M_r for these (use the periodic table inside the front cover):
   a) Ca   b) Ag   c) CO_2 d) $MgCO_3$ e) Na_2CO_3 f) ZnO   g) KOH   h) NH_3
   i) butane   j) sodium chloride   k) Iron(II) chloride
9) What is the formula for calculating the percentage mass of an element in a compound?
   a) Calculate the percentage mass of oxygen in magnesium oxide, MgO
   b) Calculate the percentage mass of carbon in   i) $CaCO_3$ ii) CO_2 iii) Methane
   c) Calculate the percentage mass of metal in these oxides: i) Na_2O ii) Fe_2O_3 iii) Al_2O_3
10) What is meant by an empirical formula?
11) List the five steps of the method for finding an empirical formula (EF) from masses or %.
12) Work these out (using the periodic table):
   a) Find the EF for the iron oxide formed when 45.1g of iron reacts with 19.3g of oxygen.
   b) Find the EF for the compound formed when 227g of calcium reacts with 216g of fluorine.
   c) Find the EF for when 208.4g of carbon reacts with 41.7g of hydrogen.
   d) Find the EF when 21.9g of magnesium, 29.3g of sulphur and 58.4g of oxygen react.
13) Write down the three steps of the method for calculating reacting masses.
   a) What mass of magnesium oxide is produced when 112.1g of magnesium burns in air?
   b) What mass of sodium is needed to produce 108.2g of sodium oxide?
   c) What mass of carbon will react with hydrogen to produce 24.6g of propane?
14) What mass of gas occupies 24 litres at room temperature and pressure?
15) Write down the formula for calculating the volume of a known mass of gas (at room T & P).
   a) What is the volume of 56.0g of nitrogen at room T & P?
   b) Find the volume of carbon dioxide produced when 5.6g of carbon is completely burned.
   c) What volume of oxygen will react with 25.0g of hydrogen to produce water?
   d) What is the mass of 5.4 litres of nitrogen gas?
   e) What mass of carbon dioxide is produced when 4.7 litres of oxygen reacts with carbon?
16) Write down the three steps for electrolysis calculations.
   a) In the electrolysis of NaCl, find the mass of Cl_2 released if 3.4g of sodium are collected.
   b) In the electrolysis of copper(II) chloride, what volume of chlorine gas would be produced for every 100g of copper obtained?
17) What is a mole? Why is it that precise number? Why does it have such a silly name?
18) How much does one mole of any compound weigh? What is meant by molar mass?
19) What is the molar volume of a gas? What is meant by a "1 molar" or "2 molar" solution?

The Evolution of the Atmosphere

The present composition of the atmosphere is: <u>78% Nitrogen</u>, <u>21% oxygen</u>, <u>0.04% CO_2</u> (= 99.04%). The remaining 1% is made up of noble gases (mainly argon). In addition there can be a lot of water vapour. But the atmosphere wasn't <u>always</u> like this. Here's how the first 4.5 billion years have gone:

Phase 1 — Volcanoes gave out Steam, CO_2, NH_3 and CH_4

The First Billion Years

Steam CO_2 CO_2 NH_3 CH_4

1) The Earth's surface was originally <u>molten</u> for many millions of years. Any atmosphere <u>boiled away</u>.
2) Eventually it cooled and a <u>thin crust</u> formed but <u>volcanoes</u> kept erupting.
3) They belched out mostly <u>carbon dioxide</u>.
4) But also some <u>steam</u>, <u>ammonia</u> and <u>methane</u>.
5) The early atmosphere was <u>mostly CO_2</u>. *+ some CO*
6) There was virtually <u>no oxygen</u>.
7) The water vapour <u>condensed</u> to form the <u>oceans</u>.
8) <u>Holiday report</u>: Not a nice place to be. Take strong walking boots and a good coat.

Phase 2 — Green Plants Evolved and produced Oxygen

The Next Two Billion Years

O_2 O_2 O_2 O_2 O_2 O_2 O_2 O_2

1) <u>Green plants</u> evolved over most of the Earth.
2) They were quite happy in the <u>CO_2 atmosphere</u>.
3) A lot of the early CO_2 <u>dissolved</u> into the oceans.
4) But the <u>green plants</u> steadily <u>removed CO_2</u> and <u>produced O_2</u> by photosynthesis.
5) Much of the CO_2 from the air thus became <u>locked up</u> in <u>fossil fuels</u> and <u>sedimentary rocks</u>.
6) <u>Methane</u> and <u>ammonia</u> reacted with the <u>oxygen</u>, releasing <u>nitrogen gas</u>.
7) Ammonia was also converted into <u>nitrates</u> by nitrifying bacteria.
8) <u>Nitrogen gas</u> was also released by <u>living organisms</u> like denitrifying bacteria.
9) <u>Holiday Report</u>: A bit slimy underfoot. Take wellies and a lot of suncream.

Phase 3 — Ozone Layer allows Evolution of Complex Animals

The Last Billion Years or so

Nice safe OZONE, O_3

1) The build-up of <u>oxygen</u> in the atmosphere <u>killed off</u> early organisms that couldn't tolerate it.
2) It also enabled the <u>evolution</u> of more <u>complex</u> organisms that <u>made use</u> of the oxygen.
3) The oxygen also created the <u>ozone layer</u> (O_3) which <u>blocked</u> harmful rays from the sun and <u>enabled</u> even <u>more complex</u> organisms to evolve.
4) There is virtually <u>no CO_2</u> left now.
5) <u>Holiday report</u>: A nice place to be. Get there before the crowds ruin it.

Coo... 4½ Billion Years — just takes your breath away...

I think it's pretty amazing how much the atmosphere has changed. It makes our present day obsession about the CO_2 going up from 0.03% to 0.04% seem a bit ridiculous, doesn't it! Anyway, never mind that, just <u>learn the three phases with all their details</u>. You don't have to draw the diagrams — although thinking about it, it's a pretty good way to remember it all, don't you think. Yip.

Today's Atmosphere and Oceans

The atmosphere we have today is just right.
It has gradually evolved over billions of years and we have evolved with it. All very slowly. It's been about the same for the past 200 million years. We worry that we're changing it for the worse by releasing various gases from industrial activity. There are three main worries: The Greenhouse Effect, The Ozone Layer and Acid Rain. These are described on the next page. (And in more detail in the Biology Book.)

Composition of Today's Atmosphere

Present composition of the atmosphere:

(That comes to over 100% because the first three are rounded up very slightly)

78%	Nitrogen	} (Often written as 79% Nitrogen for simplicity.)
1%	Argon	
21%	Oxygen	
0.04%	Carbon dioxide	

Also :
1) Varying amounts of *WATER VAPOUR*.
2) And other *noble gases* in very small amounts.

A Simple Experiment to find the % of Oxygen in the Air

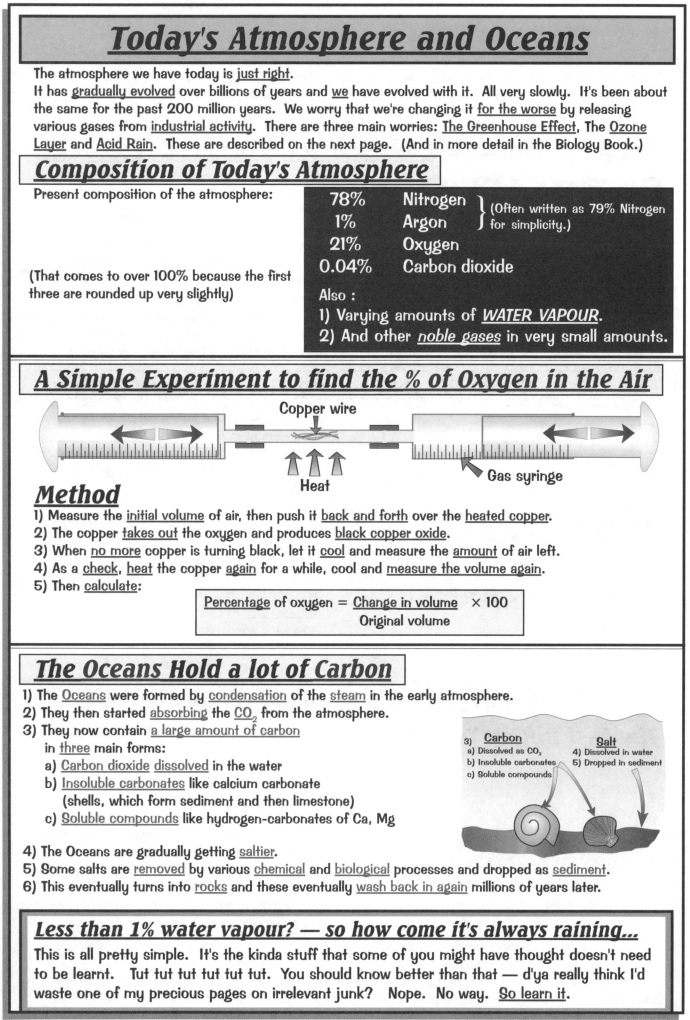

Copper wire

Heat

Gas syringe

Method

1) Measure the initial volume of air, then push it back and forth over the heated copper.
2) The copper takes out the oxygen and produces black copper oxide.
3) When no more copper is turning black, let it cool and measure the amount of air left.
4) As a check, heat the copper again for a while, cool and measure the volume again.
5) Then calculate:

$$\text{Percentage of oxygen} = \frac{\text{Change in volume}}{\text{Original volume}} \times 100$$

The Oceans Hold a lot of Carbon

1) The Oceans were formed by condensation of the steam in the early atmosphere.
2) They then started absorbing the CO_2 from the atmosphere.
3) They now contain a large amount of carbon
   in three main forms:
   a) Carbon dioxide dissolved in the water
   b) Insoluble carbonates like calcium carbonate
      (shells, which form sediment and then limestone)
   c) Soluble compounds like hydrogen-carbonates of Ca, Mg

3) Carbon
a) Dissolved as CO_2
b) Insoluble carbonates
c) Soluble compounds

Salt
4) Dissolved in water
5) Dropped in sediment

4) The Oceans are gradually getting saltier.
5) Some salts are removed by various chemical and biological processes and dropped as sediment.
6) This eventually turns into rocks and these eventually wash back in again millions of years later.

Less than 1% water vapour? — so how come it's always raining...

This is all pretty simple. It's the kinda stuff that some of you might have thought doesn't need to be learnt. Tut tut tut tut tut tut. You should know better than that — d'ya really think I'd waste one of my precious pages on irrelevant junk? Nope. No way. So learn it.

The Carbon Cycle

The Carbon Cycle shown below is a summary of how carbon passes through various forms and is constantly recycled. It's not as bad as it looks. Well, not once you know it all anyway!

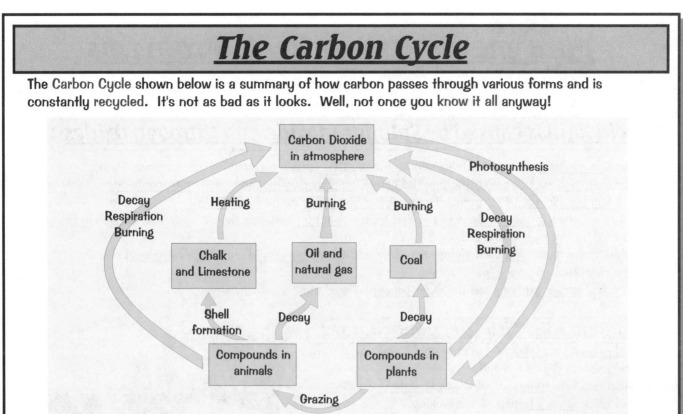

1) There's <u>another version</u> of the carbon cycle given in the <u>Biology Book</u> which is much better.
2) There are <u>many</u> different ways of representing the carbon cycle, but in the end <u>they all show the same things happening</u>. If you <u>properly understand</u> one diagram you should be able to deal with any other, even if it looks totally different. Apart from the pretty colours this is a <u>standard syllabus version</u>. That means it's like the one you'll probably get in your Exam.
3) This diagram just shows all the information, but <u>without</u> trying to make it <u>clear</u>! Look at how this relates to the one in the Biology Book, which does try to make it clear.
4) This one also contains <u>chalk</u> and <u>limestone</u> which were left out of the biology one.
5) You should learn about all these processes elsewhere. This diagram is just a <u>summary</u> of them.
6) In the Exam they could give you this diagram with <u>labels missing</u> and you'd have to <u>explain</u> or <u>describe</u> the missing process, so it's <u>pretty important</u> that you understand the <u>whole</u> thing and know about each process.

7) The blank version here is for you to <u>practise</u> on.

Cover up the original and <u>fill it all in</u> (<u>lightly</u> with a pencil), bit by bit.

<u>Keep practising</u> until you can do it. It's not as bad as it sounds. Really, it isn't.

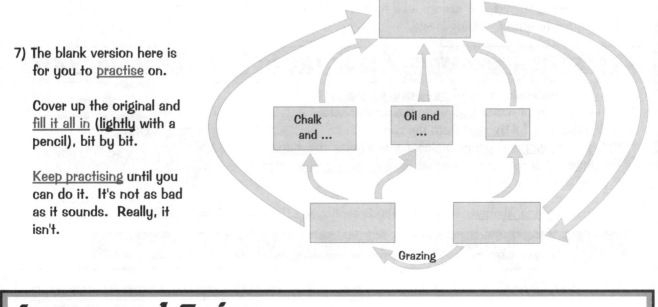

Learn and Enjoy...

The Carbon Cycle — one of the great highlights of the Double Science Syllabus, I'd say.

Man-made Atmospheric Problems

Don't confuse these three different atmospheric problems. They're all totally separate!
(The Biology Book has more details on these. Well, it has more space for pretty pictures anyway.)

1) Acid Rain is caused by Sulphur Dioxide and Nitrogen Oxides

1) When fossil fuels are burned they release mostly CO_2 (which causes the Greenhouse Effect).
2) But they also release two other harmful gases, sulphur dioxide and various nitrogen oxides.
3) The sulphur dioxide, SO_2, comes from sulphur impurities in the fossil fuels.
4) However, the nitrogen oxides are created from a reaction between the nitrogen and oxygen in the air, caused by the heat of the burning.
5) When these gases mix with clouds they form dilute sulphuric acid and dilute nitric acid.
6) This then falls as acid rain.
7) Cars and power stations are the main causes of acid rain.

Acid Rain Kills Fish, Trees and Statues

1) Acid rain causes lakes to become acidic and many plants and animals die as a result.
2) Acid rain kills trees and damages limestone buildings and ruins stone statues. It's shocking.

2) The Greenhouse Effect is caused by CO_2 trapping heat

1) The Greenhouse Effect is causing the Earth to warm up very slowly.
2) It's caused mainly by a rise in the level of CO_2 in the atmosphere due to the burning of massive amounts of fossil fuels in the last two hundred years or so.
3) The carbon dioxide (and a few other gases) trap the heat that reaches Earth from the sun.
4) This will cause a rise in temperature which is then likely to cause changes in climate and weather patterns all over the world and possible flooding due to the polar ice caps melting.
5) The level of CO_2 in the atmosphere has gone up by about 20%, and will continue to rise as long as we keep burning fossil fuels, as the graph clearly shows.
6) Deforestation is not helping either.
7) The increased concentration of CO_2 in the atmosphere means the ocean surfaces absorb a bit more CO_2, but not enough to stop the rising levels.

3) CFCs (from aerosols) Cause The Hole in The Ozone Layer

1) Ozone is a molecule made of three oxygen atoms, O_3
2) There's a layer of ozone high up in the atmosphere.
3) It absorbs harmful UV rays from the sun.
4) CFC gases react with ozone molecules and break them up.
5) This thinning of the ozone layer allows harmful UV rays to reach the surface of the Earth.

But this has nothing whatever to do with the Greenhouse Effect or acid rain. Don't mix them up:

CFCs = OZONE LAYER	CO_2 = GREENHOUSE EFFECT	SO_2 and NO_x = ACID RAIN

Eee, problems, problems — there's always summat goin' wrong...

It's a bit surprising just how much stuff there is on these environmental problems, but I'm afraid there's plenty of past Exam questions which ask precisely these details. If you want those marks, you've gotta learn these drivelly facts, and that's that. You know the drill: learn, cover, scribble, check... learn...

The Three Different Types of Rocks

Rocks shouldn't be confusing. There are three different types: sedimentary, metamorphic and igneous. Over millions of years they change from one into another. This is called the Rock Cycle. Astonishingly.

The Rock Cycle

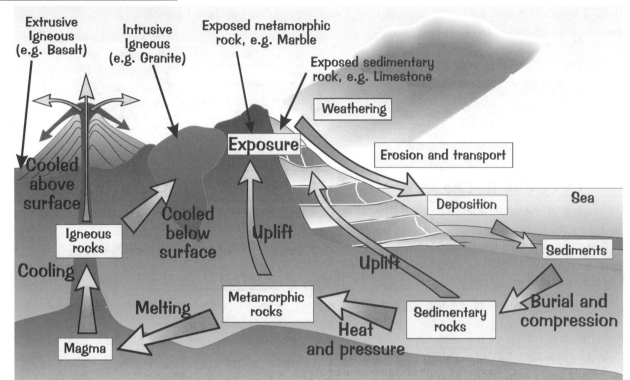

The Rocks Change from One to Another in a Slow Cycle

1) Particles get washed to the sea and settle as sediment.
2) Over millions of years these sediments get crushed into SEDIMENTARY rocks (hence the name).
3) At first they get buried, but they can either rise to the surface again to be discovered, or they can descend into the heat and pressure below.
4) If they descend, the heat and pressure completely alter the structure of the rock and they then become METAMORPHIC ROCKS (as in "metamorphosis" or "change". Another good name!).
5) These metamorphic rocks can either rise to the surface to be discovered by an enthusiastic geologist or else descend still further into the fiery abyss of the Earth's raging inferno where they will melt and become magma.
6) When magma reaches the surface it cools and sets and is then called IGNEOUS ROCK.
   ("igneous" as in "ignite" or "fire" — another cool name. Gee, if only biology names were this sensible.)
7) There are actually two types of igneous rock:
   1) EXTRUSIVE when it comes straight out of the surface from a volcano ("Ex-" as in "Exit").
   2) INTRUSIVE when it just sets as a big lump below the surface ("In-" as in "inside")
       (I have to say — whoever invented these names deserves a medal)
8) When any of these rocks reach the surface, then weathering begins and they gradually get worn down and carried off to the sea and the whole cycle starts over again... Simple, innit?

Rocks are a mystery — no, no, it's sedimentary my Dear Watson...

Don't you think the Rock Cycle is pretty ace? Can you think of anything you'd rather do than go on a family holiday to Cornwall, gazing at the cliffs and marvelling at the different types of rocks and stuff? Exactly. (And even if you can, it's still a good plan to learn about rocks.)

Sedimentary Rocks

Three steps in the Formation of Sedimentary Rocks

1) Sedimentary rocks are formed from layers of sediment laid down in lakes or seas.
2) Over millions of years the layers get buried under more layers and the weight pressing down squeezes out the water.
3) As the water disappears, salts crystallize out and cement the particles together.

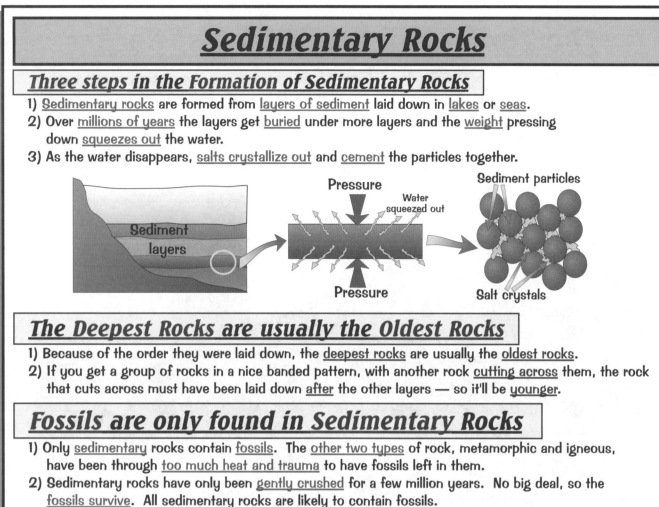

The Deepest Rocks are usually the Oldest Rocks

1) Because of the order they were laid down, the deepest rocks are usually the oldest rocks.
2) If you get a group of rocks in a nice banded pattern, with another rock cutting across them, the rock that cuts across must have been laid down after the other layers — so it'll be younger.

Fossils are only found in Sedimentary Rocks

1) Only sedimentary rocks contain fossils. The other two types of rock, metamorphic and igneous, have been through too much heat and trauma to have fossils left in them.
2) Sedimentary rocks have only been gently crushed for a few million years. No big deal, so the fossils survive. All sedimentary rocks are likely to contain fossils.
3) Fossils are a very useful way of identifying rocks as being of the same age.
4) This is because the fossilised remains that are found change (due to evolution) as the ages pass.
5) This means that if two rocks have the same fossils they must be from the same age.
6) However, if the fossils in two rocks are different, it proves nothing don't forget!

The Four Main Sedimentary Rocks:

Sedimentary rocks tend to look similar to the original sediments from which they formed.
After all, very little has happened other than them squashing together.

1) Sandstone

This is formed from sand of course. And it looks like it too. Sandstone just looks like sand particles all stuck very firmly together. There's red sandstone and yellow sandstone which are commonly used for buildings. The now famous Barrow Town Hall is built in red sandstone.

2) Limestone

This formed from seashells. It's mostly calcium carbonate and grey/white in colour. The original shells are mostly crushed but there are still quite a few fossilised shells to be found in limestone.

3) Mudstone or shale

This was formed from mud which basically means finer particles than sand.
It's often dark grey and tends to split into the original layers very easily.

4) Conglomerates

These look like a sort of crude concrete, containing pebbles set into a cement of finer particles.

Revision Pressure — don't get crushed by it...

Quite a lot of facts here on sedimentary rocks. You've gotta learn how they form, how to tell which are older, that they contain fossils, and also the names etc. of the four examples. Most important you need to be able to describe in words what they all look like. Even if you don't really know, just learn the descriptions!

Metamorphic Rocks

Heat and Pressure over Thousands of Years

Metamorphic rocks are formed by the action of heat and pressure on existing (sedimentary) rocks over long periods of time. You know that the rocks are changed versions of other rocks, because they have the same chemical compositions.

1) Earth movements can push all types of rock deep underground.

2) Here they are compressed and heated, and the mineral structure and texture may change.

3) So long as they don't actually melt they are classed as metamorphic rocks.

4) If they melt and turn to magma, they're gone. The magma may resurface as igneous rocks.

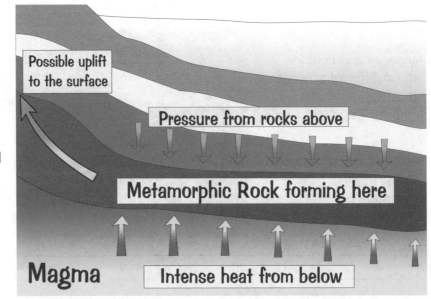

Possible uplift to the surface

Pressure from rocks above

Metamorphic Rock forming here

Magma

Intense heat from below

Slate, Marble and Schist are Metamorphic Rocks

1) Slate is formed from mudstone or clay

1) As the mudstone gets heated and compressed its tiny plate-like particles align in the same direction.
2) This allows the resulting slate to be split along that direction into thin sheets which make ideal roofing material.
3) The increasingly famous Barrow Town Hall has a slate roof.

2) Marble is formed from Limestone

1) Very high temperature will break down the shells in limestone and they reform as small crystals.
2) This gives marble a more even texture and makes it much harder.
3) It can be polished up and often has attractive patterning.
4) This makes it a great decorative stone. My Uncle Cyril has a fabulous Marble Headstone.

3) Schist is Formed when Mudstone gets real hot

1) Mudstone will turn to slate only if there's plenty of pressure but not too much heat.
2) If mudstone gets really hot, new minerals like mica start to form and create layers.
3) This creates Schist, a rock containing bands of interlocking crystals.
4) These layers of crystals are typical of a metamorphic rock.
5) Only steady heat and pressure will cause this to happen.

Schist! — when the heat and pressure is all too much...

There's quite a lot of names accumulating now. Somehow, you've got to make sense of them in your head. It really does help if you know what these rocks actually look like in real life.
It's best if you can think of specific objects made of them. Otherwise, it'll all get pretty tricky.

Igneous Rocks

Igneous Rocks are formed from Fresh Magma

1) Igneous rocks form when molten magma pushes up into the crust or right through it.

2) Igneous rocks contain various different minerals in randomly-arranged interlocking crystals.

3) There are two types of igneous rocks: EXTRUSIVE and INTRUSIVE:

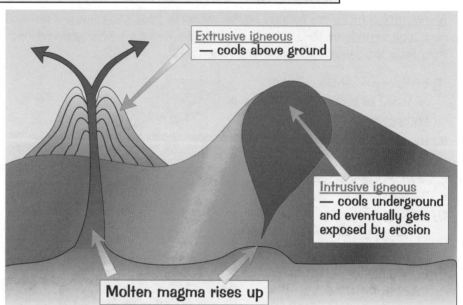

Extrusive igneous — cools above ground

Intrusive igneous — cools underground and eventually gets exposed by erosion

Molten magma rises up

INTRUSIVE igneous rocks cool SLOWLY with BIG crystals

GRANITE is an intrusive igneous rock with big crystals

1) Granite is formed underground where the magma cools down slowly.
2) This means it has big randomly-arranged crystals because it cools down slowly.
3) Granite is a very hard and decorative stone ideal for steps and buildings.
4) Barrow Town Hall? Don't know.

EXTRUSIVE igneous rocks cool QUICKLY with SMALL crystals

BASALT is an extrusive igneous rock with small crystals

1) Basalt is formed on top of the Earth's crust after bursting out of a volcano.
2) This means it has relatively small crystals — because it cooled quickly.

Identifying Rocks in Exam Questions

A typical question will simply describe a rock and ask you to identify it. Make sure you learn the information on rocks well enough to work backwards, as it were, so that you can identify the type of rock from a description. Practise by doing these:

Rock A: Small crystals in layers.
Rock B: Contains fossils.
Rock C: Randomly arranged crystals of various types.
Rock D: Hard, smooth and with wavy layers of crystals.
Rock E: Large crystals. Very hard wearing.
Rock F: Sandy texture. Fairly soft.

Answers
A: metamorphic
B: sedimentary
C: igneous
D: metamorphic
E: igneous (granite)
F: Sedimentary (sandstone)

Igneous Rocks are real cool — or they're magma...

It's very important that you know what granite looks like. You really should insist that "Teach" organises a field trip to see the famous pink granite coast of Brittany. About two weeks should be enough time to fully appreciate it. In May. Failing that, sit and learn this page in cold grey England for ten minutes.

Weathering and the Water Cycle

(Sounds like an episode from "Last of The Summer Wine" — you can just picture the whole 30 minutes of it...)

Weathering is the process of breaking rocks up

There are three distinct ways that rocks are broken up into small fragments:

A) Physical weathering is caused by ice in cracks

1) Rain water seeps into cracks in rocks and if the temperature drops below freezing, the water turns to ice and the expansion pushes the rocks apart.
2) This keeps happening each time the water thaws and refreezes.
3) Eventually bits of rock will break off.

B) Chemical weathering is caused by acidic rain on limestone

1) This isn't just "acid rain" caused by pollution. Ordinary rain is weakly acidic anyway, so it very gradually dissolves all limestone.

C) Biological weathering is caused by plant roots in cracks

1) Plants push their roots through cracks in rocks and as the roots grow they gradually push the rocks apart.

Erosion and Transport

1) Erosion is the wearing away of exposed rocks, by any means. It's different from weathering.
2) Transport is the process of carrying away the rock fragments, either falling away due to gravity, or being carried away by rivers. The rocks travelling down rivers get worn down as they go and they also wear away the river bed causing river valleys. The Grand Canyon is a grand example.

The Water Cycle

rain

evaporation

transpiration

THIS IS SERIOUSLY EASY:
1) Water EVAPORATES off the sea.
2) Water TRANSPIRES from plants.
3) It turns to CLOUDS and falls as RAIN.
4) Then it RUNS BACK TO THE SEA.

FOUR EXTRA DETAILS: (which are only very slightly harder to remember than the diagram)
1) The SUN causes the evaporation of water from the sea.
2) Clouds form because: when air rises, it cools, and the water condenses out.
3) When the condensed droplets get too big they fall as rain.
4) Some water is taken up by roots and evaporates from trees without ever reaching the sea.

Page after Page of sheer toil — it can wear you down...

Ooh, this is all really easy stuff isn't it. The only tricky bit is remembering the fancy words, like "erosion" and "chemical weathering", and exactly what they are. You know, "erosion" isn't quite the same as "weathering", for example. It's the same old method though: Learn it, then cover the page, etc.

Plate Boundaries

At the <u>boundaries</u> between tectonic plates there's usually <u>trouble</u> like <u>volcanoes</u> or <u>earthquakes</u>. There are <u>three</u> different ways that plates interact: <u>Colliding</u>, <u>separating</u> or <u>sliding</u> past each other.

Oceanic and Continental Plates Colliding: The Andes

1) The <u>oceanic plate</u> is always <u>forced underneath</u> the continental plate.
2) This is called a <u>subduction zone</u>.
3) As the oceanic crust is pushed down it <u>melts</u> and <u>pressure builds up</u> due to all the melting rock.
4) This <u>molten rock</u> finds its way to the <u>surface</u> and <u>volcanoes</u> form.
5) There are also <u>earthquakes</u> as the two plates slowly <u>grind</u> past each other.
6) A <u>deep trench</u> forms on the ocean floor where the <u>oceanic plate</u> is being <u>forced down</u>.
7) The <u>continental</u> crust <u>crumples</u> and <u>folds</u> forming <u>mountains</u> at the coast.
8) The classic example of all this is the <u>west coast of South America</u> where the <u>Andes mountains</u> are. That region has <u>all the features</u>:

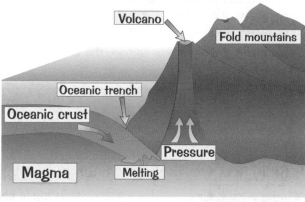

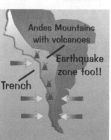

> *Volcanoes, earthquakes*, an *oceanic trench* and *mountains*.

Two Continental Plates Collide: The Himalayas

1) The <u>two continental plates</u> meet <u>head on</u>, neither one being subducted.
2) Any <u>sediment layers</u> lying between the two continent masses get <u>squeezed</u> between them.
3) These sediment layers inevitably start <u>crumpling and folding</u> and soon form into <u>big mountains</u>.
4) The <u>Himalayan mountains</u> are the classic case of this.

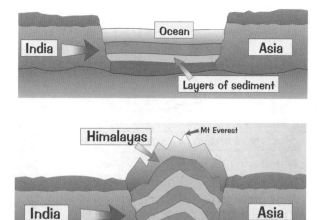

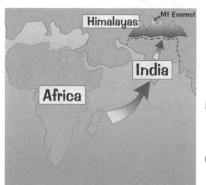

5) <u>India</u> actually <u>broke away</u> from the side of Africa and <u>piled</u> into the bottom of <u>Asia</u>, and is <u>still</u> doing so, <u>pushing the Himalayas up</u> as it goes.
6) <u>Mount Everest</u> is there and is <u>getting higher</u> by a few cm every year as India continues to push up into the continent of Asia.

Another page to learn — don't make a mountain out of it...

<u>Make sure you learn all these diagrams</u> — they summarise all the information in the text. They may well ask you for examples in the Exam, so make sure you know the two different kinds of situation that the Andes and the Himalayas actually represent. <u>Cover and scribble...</u>

Revision Summary For Section Four

Well let's face it, this section on Air and Rock is definitely the easy interlude in the Chemistry syllabus. In the Olden Days (the 1970's) this stuff all used to be called Geography, which as you know, is a much easier subject than Chemistry. However, easy or not, there's still quite a lot of stuff to learn. Try these little jokers and see how much you know:

1) How old is the Earth? What was it like for the first billion years or so?

2) What gases did the early atmosphere consist of? Where did these gases come from?

3) What was the main thing which caused phase two of the atmosphere's evolution?

4) Which gases became much less common and which one increased?

5) Which gas allowed phase three to take place? Which gas is almost completely gone?

6) What are the percentages of gases in today's atmosphere?

7) Describe a simple experiment to find the percentage of oxygen in air.

8) Explain the three ways in which the oceans contain carbon, and two ways they contain salt.

9) What are the three man-made atmospheric problems?

10) Which gases cause acid rain? Where do they come from?
    What are the three adverse effects of acid rain?

11) Which gas causes the Greenhouse Effect? Explain how the Greenhouse Effect works.

12) Which gas is damaging the ozone layer? What are the harmful effects of this?

13) What is the carbon cycle? How much of that diagram on P. 39 can you draw from memory?

14) What are the three types of rock? Draw a full diagram of the rock cycle.

15) Explain how the three types of rock change from one to another. How long does this take?

16) Draw diagrams to show how sedimentary rocks form.

17) What are found in sedimentary rocks but are not found in any other type of rock?

18) List the four main sedimentary rocks, give a description of each, and a use for two of them.

19) Draw a diagram to show how metamorphic rocks are formed. What does the name mean?

20) What are the three main metamorphic rocks?
    Describe their appearance and give a use for two of them.

21) How are igneous rocks formed? What are the two types? Give an example of each.

22) What is the difference in the way that they formed and in their structure and appearance?

23) What are the three types of weathering? Explain the details for each type, with diagrams.

24) What exactly is "erosion"? What process is "transport"?

25) Which of these processes created the Grand Canyon or any other river valley?

26) Draw a pretty diagram of the water cycle. Explain how the whole process works.

27) What happens when an oceanic plate collides with a continental plate? Draw a diagram.

28) What four features does this produce? Which part of the world is the classic case of this?

29) What happens when two continental plates collide? Draw diagrams.

30) What features does this produce? Which part of the world is the classic case of this?

A Brief History of The Periodic Table

The early Chemists were keen to try and find <u>patterns</u> in the elements.
The <u>more</u> elements that were identified, the <u>easier</u> it became to find patterns of course.

In the Early 1800s They Could Only go on Atomic Mass

They had <u>two</u> obvious ways to categorise elements:

1) Their <u>physical</u> and <u>chemical</u> properties	2) Their <u>Relative Atomic Mass</u>

1) Remember, they had <u>no idea</u> of <u>atomic structure</u> or of protons or electrons, so there was <u>no such thing</u> as <u>atomic number</u> to them. (It was only in the 20th Century after protons and electrons were discovered, that it was realised the elements should be arranged in order of <u>atomic number</u>.)
2) But <u>back then</u>, the only thing they could measure was <u>Relative Atomic Mass</u> and the only obvious way to arrange the known elements was <u>in order of atomic mass</u>.
3) When this was done a <u>periodic pattern</u> was noticed in the <u>properties</u> of the elements.

Newlands' Octaves Were The First Good Effort

A chap called <u>Newlands</u> had the first good stab at it in <u>1863</u>. He noticed that every <u>eighth</u> element had similar properties and so he listed some of the known elements in rows of seven:

Li	Be	B	C	N	O	F
Na	Mg	Al	Si	P	S	Cl

These sets of eight were called <u>Newlands' Octaves</u> but unfortunately the pattern <u>broke down</u> on the <u>third row</u> with many <u>transition metals</u> like Fe, Cu and Zn messing it up completely.
It was because he left <u>no gaps</u> that his work was <u>ignored</u>.
But he was getting <u>pretty close</u>, as you can see.

Dmitri Mendeleyev Left Gaps and Predicted New Elements

1) In <u>1869</u>, <u>Dmitri Mendeleyev</u> in Russia, armed with about 50 known elements, arranged them into his Table of Elements with various <u>gaps</u>, as shown.
2) Mendeleyev ordered the elements in order of <u>atomic mass</u> (like Newlands did).
3) But Mendeleyev found he had to leave <u>gaps</u> in order to keep elements with <u>similar properties</u> in the same <u>vertical groups</u> — and he was prepared to leave some <u>very big gaps</u> in the first two rows before the transition metals come in on the <u>third</u> row.

The <u>gaps</u> were the really clever bit because they <u>predicted</u> the properties of so far <u>undiscovered elements</u>.

When they were found and they <u>fitted the pattern</u> it was pretty smashing news for old Dmitri. The old rogue.

Mendeleyev's Table of the Elements

H																	
Li	Be												B	C	N	O	F
Na	Mg												Al	Si	P	S	Cl
K	Ca	*	Ti	V	Cr	Mn	Fe	Co	Ni	Cu	Zn	*	*	As	Se	Br	
Rb	Sr	Y	Zr	Nb	Mo	*	Ru	Rh	Pd	Ag	Cd	In	Sn	Sb	Te	I	
Cs	Ba	*	*	Ta	W	*	Os	Ir	Pt	Au	Hg	Tl	Pb	Bi			

I can't see what all the fuss is — it all seems quite elementary...

They're quite into having bits of History in Science now. They like to think you'll gain an appreciation of the role of science in the overall progress of human society. Personally, I'm not that bothered whether you do or not. All I wanna know is: <u>Have you learnt all the facts yet?</u> And if not — <u>WHY NOT?</u> HUH?

The Periodic Table

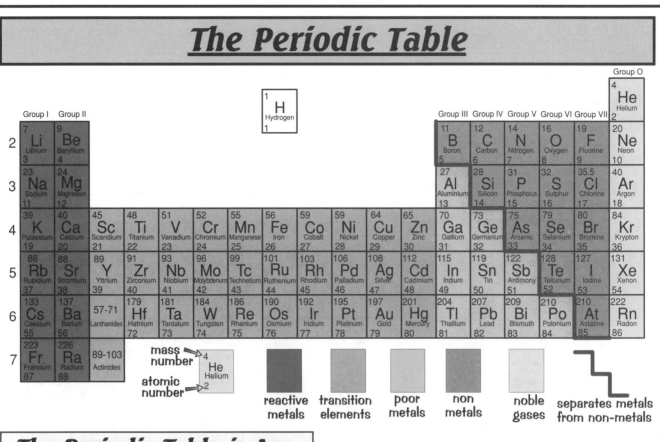

reactive metals | transition elements | poor metals | non metals | noble gases | separates metals from non-metals

The Periodic Table is Ace

1) There are 100ish elements, which all materials are made of. More are still being discovered.
2) The modern Periodic Table shows the elements in order of atomic number.
3) The Periodic Table is laid out so that elements with similar properties form in columns.
4) These vertical columns are called Groups and Roman Numerals are often used for them.
5) For example the Group II elements are Be, Mg, Ca, Sr, Ba and Ra.
   They're all metals which form 2+ ions and they have many other similar properties.
6) The rows are called periods. Each new period represents another full shell of electrons.

The Elements of a Group Have the Same Outer Electrons

1) The elements in each Group all have the same number of electrons in their outer shell.
2) That's why they have similar properties. And that's why we arrange them in this way.
3) You absolutely must get that into your head if you want to understand any Chemistry.

> The properties of the elements are decided *entirely* by how many electrons they have.
> Atomic number is therefore very significant because it is equal to how many electrons each atom has.
> But it's the number of electrons in the *outer shell* which is the really important thing.

Electron Shells are just Totally Brill

The fact that electrons form shells around atoms is the reason for the whole of chemistry.
If they just whizzed round the nucleus any old how and didn't care about shells or any of that stuff there'd be no chemical reactions. No nothing in fact — because nothing would happen.
Without shells there'd be no atoms wanting to gain, lose or share electrons to form full shell arrangements. So they wouldn't be interested in forming ions or covalent bonds. Nothing would bother and nothing would happen. The atoms would just slob about, all day long. Just like teenagers.
But amazingly, they *do* form shells (if they didn't, we wouldn't even be here to wonder about it), and the electron arrangement of each atom determines the whole of its chemical behaviour.
Phew. I mean electron arrangements explain practically the whole Universe. They're just totally brill.

Electron Shells — where would we be without them...

Make sure you learn the whole periodic table including every name, symbol and number.
No, only kidding!   Just learn the numbered points and scribble them down, mini-essay style.

Electron Arrangements

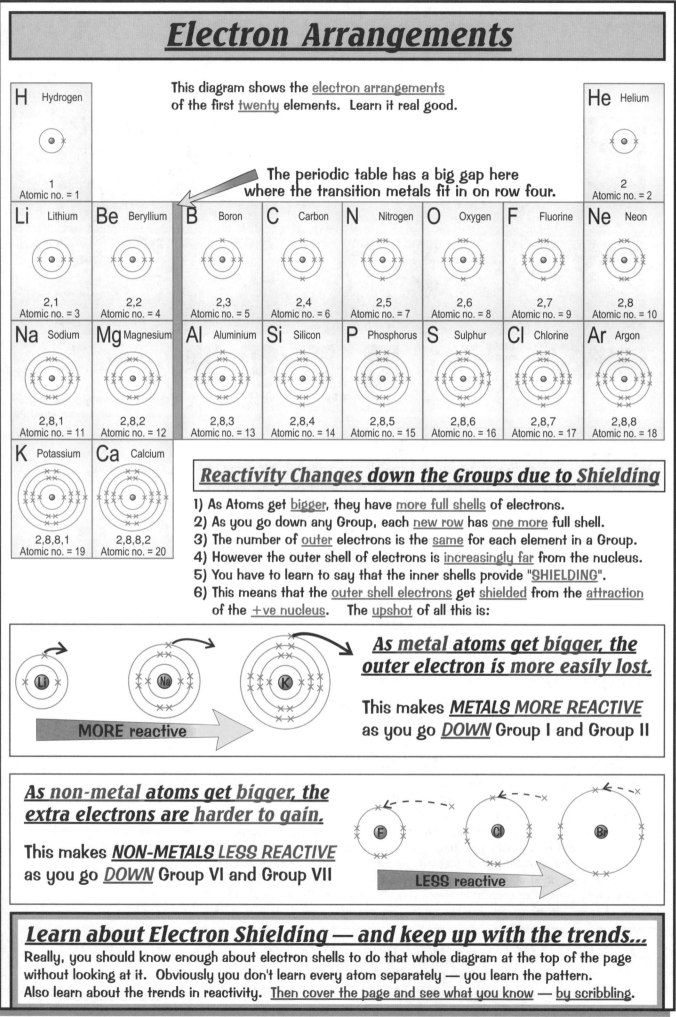

This diagram shows the electron arrangements of the first twenty elements. Learn it real good.

The periodic table has a big gap here where the transition metals fit in on row four.

H Hydrogen							He Helium
1 Atomic no. = 1							2 Atomic no. = 2

Li Lithium	Be Beryllium	B Boron	C Carbon	N Nitrogen	O Oxygen	F Fluorine	Ne Neon
2,1 Atomic no. = 3	2,2 Atomic no. = 4	2,3 Atomic no. = 5	2,4 Atomic no. = 6	2,5 Atomic no. = 7	2,6 Atomic no. = 8	2,7 Atomic no. = 9	2,8 Atomic no. = 10

Na Sodium	Mg Magnesium	Al Aluminium	Si Silicon	P Phosphorus	S Sulphur	Cl Chlorine	Ar Argon
2,8,1 Atomic no. = 11	2,8,2 Atomic no. = 12	2,8,3 Atomic no. = 13	2,8,4 Atomic no. = 14	2,8,5 Atomic no. = 15	2,8,6 Atomic no. = 16	2,8,7 Atomic no. = 17	2,8,8 Atomic no. = 18

K Potassium	Ca Calcium
2,8,8,1 Atomic no. = 19	2,8,8,2 Atomic no. = 20

Reactivity Changes down the Groups due to Shielding

1) As Atoms get bigger, they have more full shells of electrons.
2) As you go down any Group, each new row has one more full shell.
3) The number of outer electrons is the same for each element in a Group.
4) However the outer shell of electrons is increasingly far from the nucleus.
5) You have to learn to say that the inner shells provide "SHIELDING".
6) This means that the outer shell electrons get shielded from the attraction of the +ve nucleus. The upshot of all this is:

MORE reactive

As metal atoms get bigger, the outer electron is more easily lost.

This makes METALS MORE REACTIVE as you go DOWN Group I and Group II

As non-metal atoms get bigger, the extra electrons are harder to gain.

This makes NON-METALS LESS REACTIVE as you go DOWN Group VI and Group VII

LESS reactive

Learn about Electron Shielding — and keep up with the trends...

Really, you should know enough about electron shells to do that whole diagram at the top of the page without looking at it. Obviously you don't learn every atom separately — you learn the pattern. Also learn about the trends in reactivity. Then cover the page and see what you know — by scribbling.

Group 0 — The Noble Gases

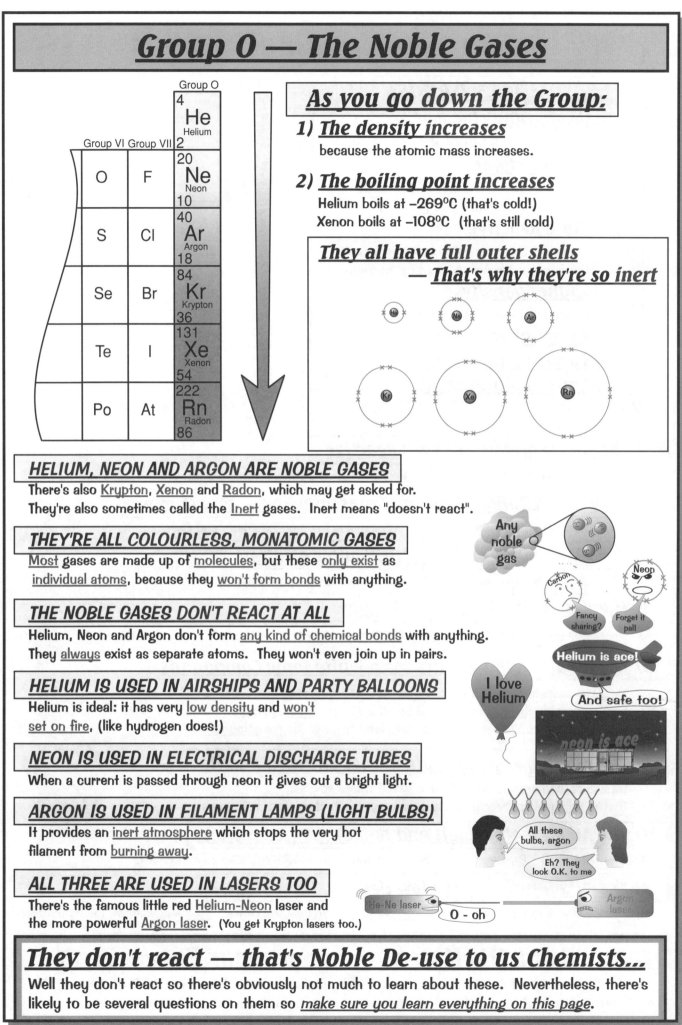

As you go down the Group:

1) The density increases
because the atomic mass increases.

2) The boiling point increases
Helium boils at –269°C (that's cold!)
Xenon boils at –108°C (that's still cold)

They all have full outer shells
— That's why they're so inert

HELIUM, NEON AND ARGON ARE NOBLE GASES

There's also Krypton, Xenon and Radon, which may get asked for.
They're also sometimes called the Inert gases. Inert means "doesn't react".

THEY'RE ALL COLOURLESS, MONATOMIC GASES

Most gases are made up of molecules, but these only exist as
individual atoms, because they won't form bonds with anything.

THE NOBLE GASES DON'T REACT AT ALL

Helium, Neon and Argon don't form any kind of chemical bonds with anything.
They always exist as separate atoms. They won't even join up in pairs.

HELIUM IS USED IN AIRSHIPS AND PARTY BALLOONS

Helium is ideal: it has very low density and won't
set on fire, (like hydrogen does!)

NEON IS USED IN ELECTRICAL DISCHARGE TUBES

When a current is passed through neon it gives out a bright light.

ARGON IS USED IN FILAMENT LAMPS (LIGHT BULBS)

It provides an inert atmosphere which stops the very hot
filament from burning away.

ALL THREE ARE USED IN LASERS TOO

There's the famous little red Helium-Neon laser and
the more powerful Argon laser. (You get Krypton lasers too.)

They don't react — that's Noble De-use to us Chemists...

Well they don't react so there's obviously not much to learn about these. Nevertheless, there's
likely to be several questions on them so make sure you learn everything on this page.

Group I — The Alkali Metals

Learn These Trends:

As you go _DOWN_ Group I,
the Alkali Metals become:

1) _Bigger atoms_
...because there's one extra full shell of electrons for each row you go down.

2) _More Reactive_
...because the outer electron is more easily lost, because it's further from the nucleus.

3) _Higher density_
because the atoms have more mass.

4) _Even Softer to cut_
5) _Lower melting point_
6) _Lower boiling point_

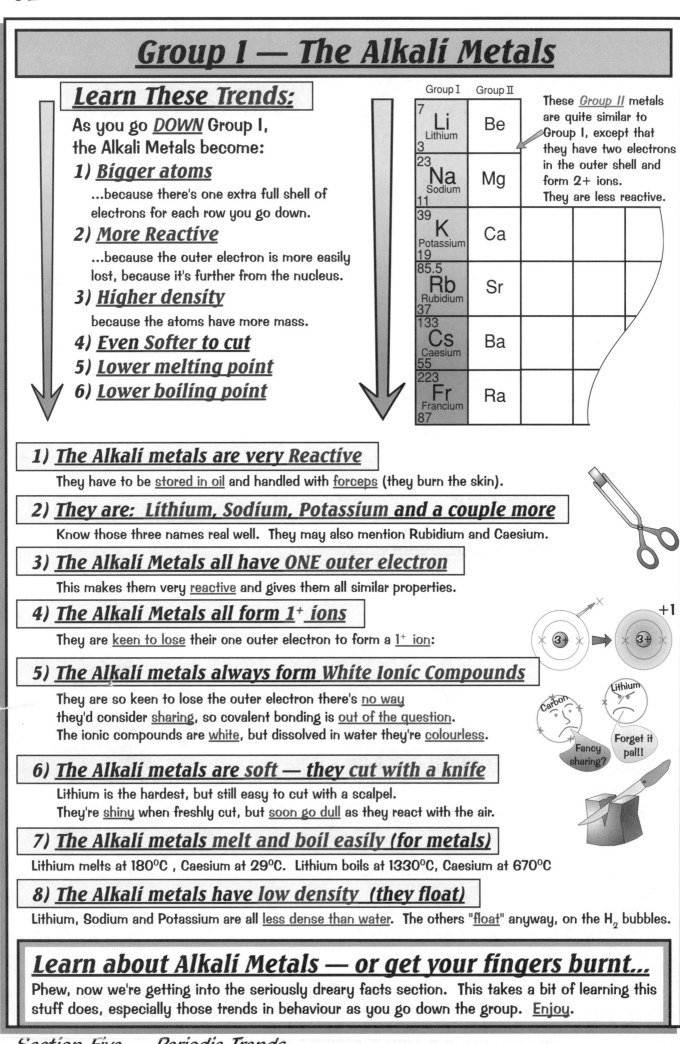

Group I	Group II
7 Li Lithium 3	Be
23 Na Sodium 11	Mg
39 K Potassium 19	Ca
85.5 Rb Rubidium 37	Sr
133 Cs Caesium 55	Ba
223 Fr Francium 87	Ra

These _Group II_ metals are quite similar to Group I, except that they have two electrons in the outer shell and form 2+ ions.
They are less reactive.

1) _The Alkali metals are very Reactive_
They have to be stored in oil and handled with forceps (they burn the skin).

2) _They are: Lithium, Sodium, Potassium and a couple more_
Know those three names real well. They may also mention Rubidium and Caesium.

3) _The Alkali Metals all have ONE outer electron_
This makes them very reactive and gives them all similar properties.

4) _The Alkali Metals all form 1+ ions_
They are keen to lose their one outer electron to form a 1+ ion:

5) _The Alkali metals always form White Ionic Compounds_
They are so keen to lose the outer electron there's no way they'd consider sharing, so covalent bonding is out of the question.
The ionic compounds are white, but dissolved in water they're colourless.

6) _The Alkali metals are soft — they cut with a knife_
Lithium is the hardest, but still easy to cut with a scalpel.
They're shiny when freshly cut, but soon go dull as they react with the air.

7) _The Alkali metals melt and boil easily (for metals)_
Lithium melts at 180°C , Caesium at 29°C. Lithium boils at 1330°C, Caesium at 670°C

8) _The Alkali metals have low density (they float)_
Lithium, Sodium and Potassium are all less dense than water. The others "float" anyway, on the H_2 bubbles.

Learn about Alkali Metals — or get your fingers burnt...
Phew, now we're getting into the seriously dreary facts section. This takes a bit of learning this stuff does, especially those trends in behaviour as you go down the group. Enjoy.

Reactions of the Alkali Metals

Reaction with Cold Water produces Hydrogen Gas

1) When <u>lithium</u>, <u>sodium</u> or <u>potassium</u> are put in <u>water</u>, they react very <u>vigorously</u>.

2) They <u>move</u> around the surface, <u>fizzing</u> furiously.

3) They produce <u>hydrogen</u>. Potassium gets hot enough to <u>ignite</u> it.
   A lighted splint will <u>indicate</u> hydrogen by producing
   the notorious "<u>squeaky pop</u>" as the H_2 ignites.

4) Sodium and potassium <u>melt</u> in the heat of the reaction.

5) They form a <u>hydroxide</u> in solution, i.e. <u>aqueous OH$^-$ ions</u>.

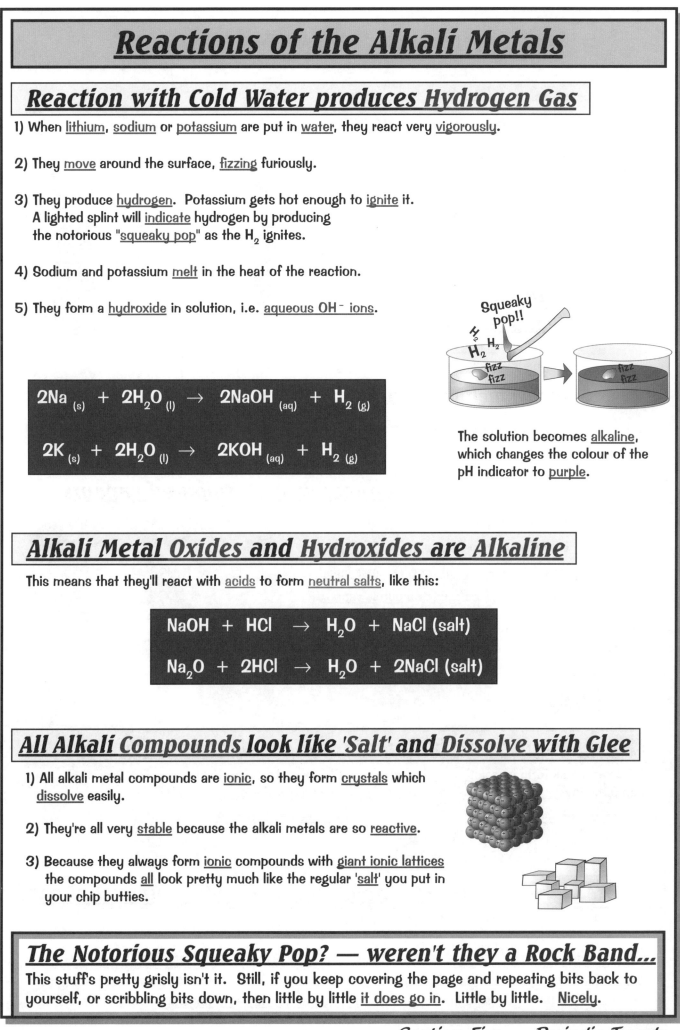

$$2Na_{(s)} + 2H_2O_{(l)} \rightarrow 2NaOH_{(aq)} + H_{2(g)}$$

$$2K_{(s)} + 2H_2O_{(l)} \rightarrow 2KOH_{(aq)} + H_{2(g)}$$

The solution becomes <u>alkaline</u>, which changes the colour of the pH indicator to <u>purple</u>.

Alkali Metal Oxides and Hydroxides are Alkaline

This means that they'll react with <u>acids</u> to form <u>neutral salts</u>, like this:

$$NaOH + HCl \rightarrow H_2O + NaCl \text{ (salt)}$$

$$Na_2O + 2HCl \rightarrow H_2O + 2NaCl \text{ (salt)}$$

All Alkali Compounds look like 'Salt' and Dissolve with Glee

1) All alkali metal compounds are <u>ionic</u>, so they form <u>crystals</u> which <u>dissolve</u> easily.

2) They're all very <u>stable</u> because the alkali metals are so <u>reactive</u>.

3) Because they always form <u>ionic</u> compounds with <u>giant ionic lattices</u> the compounds <u>all</u> look pretty much like the regular 'salt' you put in your chip butties.

The Notorious Squeaky Pop? — weren't they a Rock Band...

This stuff's pretty grisly isn't it. Still, if you keep covering the page and repeating bits back to yourself, or scribbling bits down, then little by little <u>it does go in</u>. Little by little. <u>Nicely</u>.

Group VII — The Halogens

Learn These Trends:

As you go _DOWN_ Group VII, the _HALOGENS_ become:

1) Bigger atoms
...because there's one extra full shell of electrons for each row you go down.

2) Less Reactive
...because there's less inclination to gain the extra electron to fill the outer shell when it's further out from the nucleus.

3) Darker in colour

4) They go from gas to solid
Fluorine and chlorine are gases, bromine is a liquid, and iodine is a solid.

5) Higher melting point

6) Higher boiling point

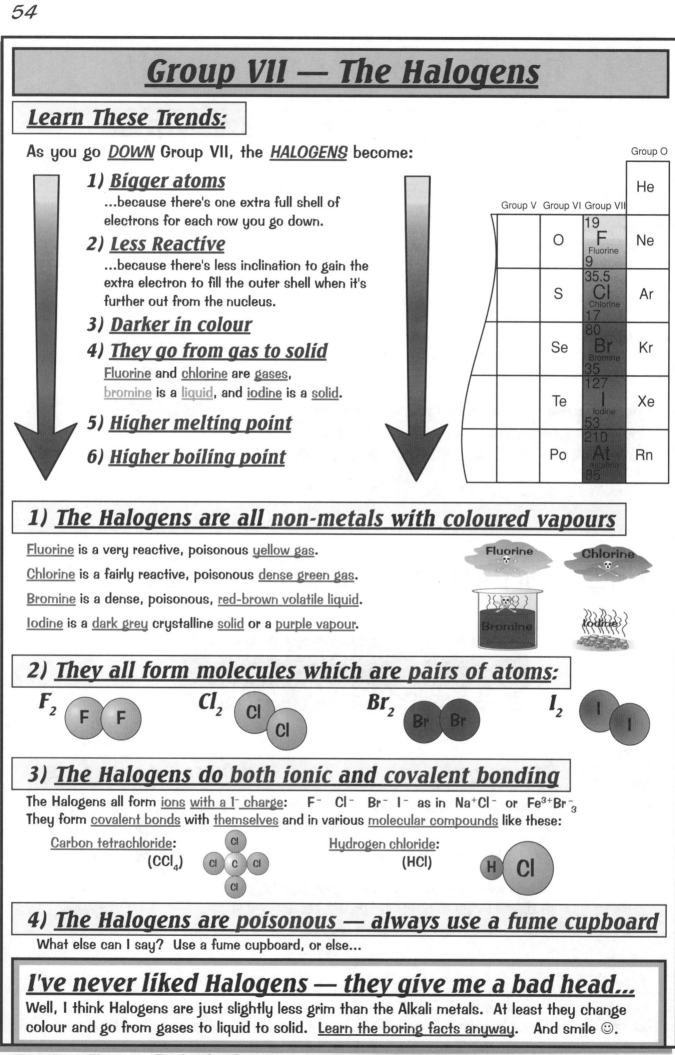

	Group V	Group VI	Group VII	Group O
				He
	O	S	$^{19}_{9}$F Fluorine	Ne
		S	$^{35.5}_{17}$Cl Chlorine	Ar
	Se		$^{80}_{35}$Br Bromine	Kr
	Te		$^{127}_{53}$I Iodine	Xe
	Po		$^{210}_{85}$At Astatine	Rn

1) The Halogens are all non-metals with coloured vapours

Fluorine is a very reactive, poisonous yellow gas.

Chlorine is a fairly reactive, poisonous dense green gas.

Bromine is a dense, poisonous, red-brown volatile liquid.

Iodine is a dark grey crystalline solid or a purple vapour.

2) They all form molecules which are pairs of atoms:

F_2 Cl_2 Br_2 I_2

3) The Halogens do both ionic and covalent bonding

The Halogens all form ions with a 1⁻ charge: F^- Cl^- Br^- I^- as in Na^+Cl^- or $Fe^{3+}Br^-_3$
They form covalent bonds with themselves and in various molecular compounds like these:

Carbon tetrachloride:
(CCl_4)

Hydrogen chloride:
(HCl)

4) The Halogens are poisonous — always use a fume cupboard

What else can I say? Use a fume cupboard, or else...

I've never liked Halogens — they give me a bad head...

Well, I think Halogens are just slightly less grim than the Alkali metals. At least they change colour and go from gases to liquid to solid. Learn the boring facts anyway.   And smile ☺.

Reactions of The Halogens

1) The Halogens react with metals to form salts

They <u>react</u> with most <u>metals</u> including <u>iron</u> and <u>aluminium</u>, to form <u>salts</u> (or "<u>metal halides</u>").

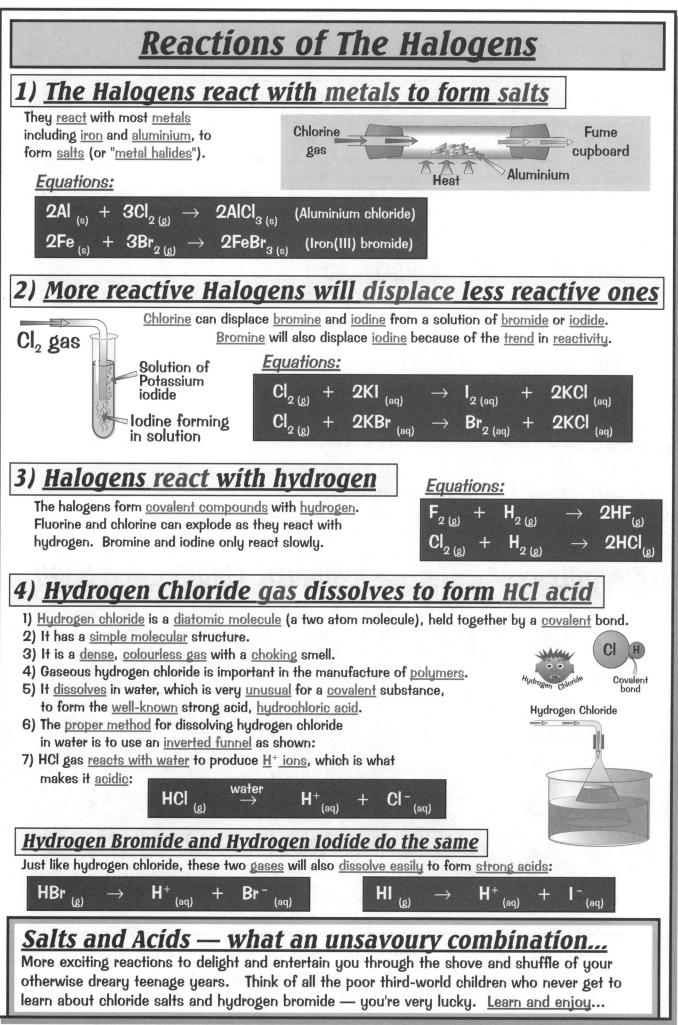

Chlorine gas   Fume cupboard

Heat   Aluminium

Equations:

$$2Al_{(s)} + 3Cl_{2(g)} \rightarrow 2AlCl_{3(s)} \quad \text{(Aluminium chloride)}$$

$$2Fe_{(s)} + 3Br_{2(g)} \rightarrow 2FeBr_{3(s)} \quad \text{(Iron(III) bromide)}$$

2) More reactive Halogens will displace less reactive ones

<u>Chlorine</u> can displace <u>bromine</u> and <u>iodine</u> from a solution of <u>bromide</u> or <u>iodide</u>. <u>Bromine</u> will also displace <u>iodine</u> because of the <u>trend</u> in <u>reactivity</u>.

Cl$_2$ gas

Solution of Potassium iodide

Iodine forming in solution

Equations:

$$Cl_{2(g)} + 2KI_{(aq)} \rightarrow I_{2(aq)} + 2KCl_{(aq)}$$

$$Cl_{2(g)} + 2KBr_{(aq)} \rightarrow Br_{2(aq)} + 2KCl_{(aq)}$$

3) Halogens react with hydrogen

The halogens form <u>covalent compounds</u> with <u>hydrogen</u>. Fluorine and chlorine can explode as they react with hydrogen. Bromine and iodine only react slowly.

Equations:

$$F_{2(g)} + H_{2(g)} \rightarrow 2HF_{(g)}$$

$$Cl_{2(g)} + H_{2(g)} \rightarrow 2HCl_{(g)}$$

4) Hydrogen Chloride gas dissolves to form HCl acid

1) <u>Hydrogen chloride</u> is a <u>diatomic molecule</u> (a two atom molecule), held together by a <u>covalent</u> bond.
2) It has a <u>simple molecular</u> structure.
3) It is a <u>dense</u>, <u>colourless gas</u> with a <u>choking</u> smell.
4) Gaseous hydrogen chloride is important in the manufacture of <u>polymers</u>.
5) It <u>dissolves</u> in water, which is very <u>unusual</u> for a <u>covalent</u> substance, to form the <u>well-known</u> strong acid, <u>hydrochloric acid</u>.
6) The <u>proper method</u> for dissolving hydrogen chloride in water is to use an <u>inverted funnel</u> as shown:
7) HCl gas <u>reacts with water</u> to produce <u>H$^+$ ions</u>, which is what makes it <u>acidic</u>:

Cl H
Covalent bond

Hydrogen Chloride

$$HCl_{(g)} \xrightarrow{\text{water}} H^+_{(aq)} + Cl^-_{(aq)}$$

Hydrogen Bromide and Hydrogen Iodide do the same

Just like hydrogen chloride, these two <u>gases</u> will also <u>dissolve easily</u> to form <u>strong acids</u>:

$$HBr_{(g)} \rightarrow H^+_{(aq)} + Br^-_{(aq)}$$

$$HI_{(g)} \rightarrow H^+_{(aq)} + I^-_{(aq)}$$

Salts and Acids — what an unsavoury combination...

More exciting reactions to delight and entertain you through the shove and shuffle of your otherwise dreary teenage years. Think of all the poor third-world children who never get to learn about chloride salts and hydrogen bromide — you're very lucky. <u>Learn and enjoy</u>...

Industrial Salt

Salt is taken from the sea — and from underneath Cheshire

1) In hot countries they just pour sea water into big flat open tanks and let the sun evaporate the water to leave salt. This is no good in cold countries because there isn't enough sunshine.

2) In Britain (a cold country — as if you need reminding), salt is extracted from underground deposits left millions of years ago when ancient seas evaporated.
There are massive deposits of this ROCK SALT in Cheshire. It's taken from underground mines. Rock salt is a mixture of mainly sand and salt. It can be used in its raw state on roads, or the salt can be filtered out for more refined uses, as detailed below.

1) Rock salt is used for de-icing roads

1) The salt in the mixture melts ice by lowering the freezing point of water to around –5°C.

2) The sand and grit in it gives useful grip on ice which hasn't melted.

2) Salt (sodium chloride) is used in the food industry, somewhat

Salt is added to most processed foods to enhance the flavour.
It's now reckoned to be unhealthy to eat too much salt.

I'm just waiting for the great day of reckoning when finally every single food has been declared either generally unhealthy or else downright dangerous. Perhaps we should all lay bets on what'll be the last food still considered safe to eat. My money's on Dried Locusts.

3) Salt is used for making chemicals

Salt is important for the chemicals industries, which are mostly based around Cheshire and Merseyside because of all the rock salt there. The first thing they do is electrolyse it like this:

Electrolysis of Salt gives Hydrogen, Chlorine and NaOH

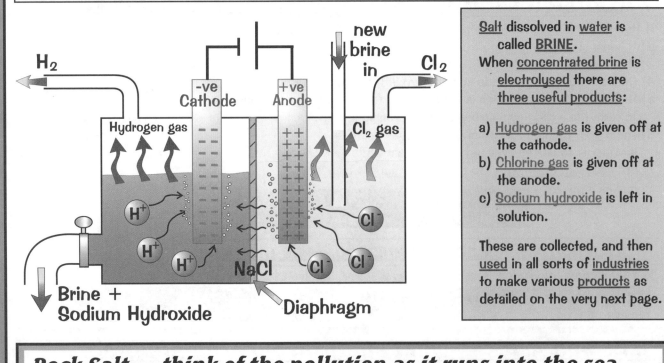

Salt dissolved in water is called BRINE.

When concentrated brine is electrolysed there are three useful products:

a) Hydrogen gas is given off at the cathode.

b) Chlorine gas is given off at the anode.

c) Sodium hydroxide is left in solution.

These are collected, and then used in all sorts of industries to make various products as detailed on the very next page.

Rock Salt — think of the pollution as it runs into the sea...

Look at this page. There's all that writing but only about 10 important facts to learn in the whole lot. Hmm, I guess that's my fault — too much drivel. Still, if it makes you smile occasionally...

Uses of Halogens and Salt Products

Some Uses of Halogens you Really Should Know

Fluorine, (or rather fluoride) reduces dental decay

Fluorides can be added to drinking water and toothpastes to help prevent tooth decay.

Chlorine is used in bleach and for sterilising water

1) Chlorine dissolved in sodium hydroxide solution is called bleach.
2) Chlorine compounds are also used to kill germs in swimming pools and drinking water.
3) It's also used to make insecticides and in the manufacture of HCl.

Iodine is used as an antiseptic...

...but it stings like nobody's business and stains the skin brown. Nice.

Silver halides are used on black and white photographic film

1) Silver is very unreactive. It does form halides but they're very easily split up.
2) In fact, ordinary visible light has enough energy to do so.
3) Photographic film is coated with colourless silver bromide.
4) When light hits parts of it, the silver bromide splits up into silver and bromine:

$$2AgBr \rightarrow Br_2 + 2Ag \text{ (silver metal)}$$

5) The silver metal appears black. The brighter the light, the darker it goes.
6) This produces a black and white negative, like an X-ray picture for example.

Useful Products from the Electrolysis of Brine

1) Chlorine

1) Used in bleach, for sterilising water, for making HCl and insecticides.
2) Used to make CFCs for fridges, aerosols and plastics, but they're used a lot less now we know they damage the ozone layer.

2) Hydrogen

1) Used in the Haber Process to make ammonia.
2) Used to change oils into fats for making margarine. ("hydrogenated vegetable oil")

3) Sodium hydroxide

Sodium Hydroxide is a very strong alkali and is used widely in the chemical industry, e.g.

1) soap   2) ceramics   3) organic chemicals   4) paper pulp   5) oven cleaner.

Learn the many uses of salt — just use your brine...

Lots of seriously tedious facts to learn here. And virtually no nonsense. But think about it, the only bit you're gonna really remember forever is that bit about iodine. Am I right or am I right?

Acids and Alkalis

The pH Scale and Universal Indicator

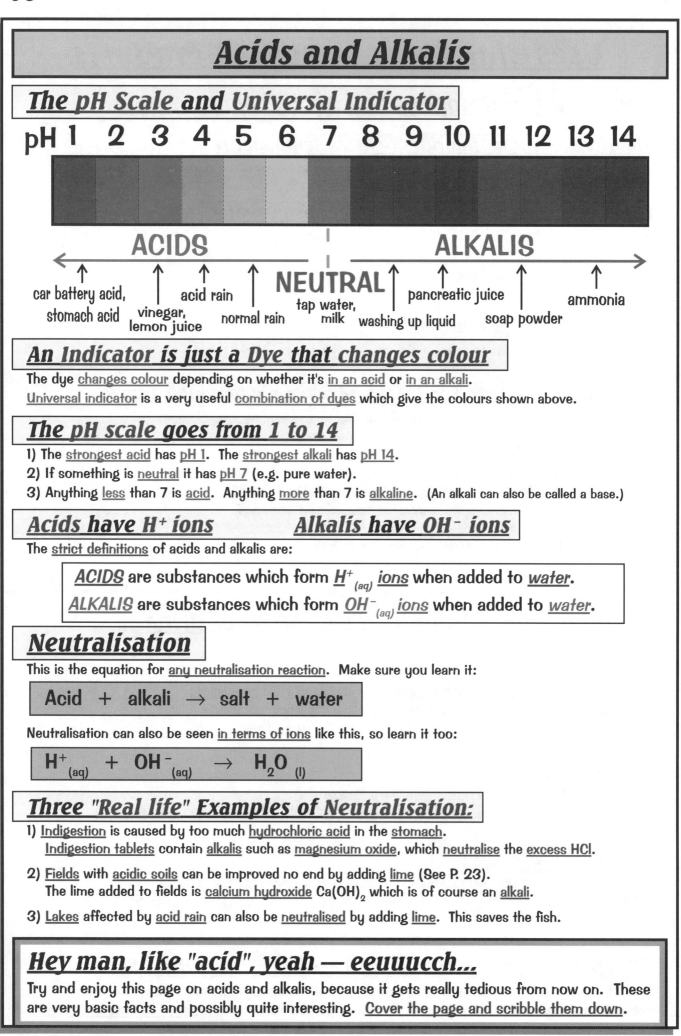

pH 1 2 3 4 5 6 7 8 9 10 11 12 13 14

← ACIDS   NEUTRAL   ALKALIS →

car battery acid, stomach acid

vinegar, lemon juice

acid rain

normal rain

tap water, milk

washing up liquid

pancreatic juice

soap powder

ammonia

An Indicator is just a Dye that changes colour

The dye changes colour depending on whether it's in an acid or in an alkali.

Universal indicator is a very useful combination of dyes which give the colours shown above.

The pH scale goes from 1 to 14

1) The strongest acid has pH 1. The strongest alkali has pH 14.

2) If something is neutral it has pH 7 (e.g. pure water).

3) Anything less than 7 is acid. Anything more than 7 is alkaline. (An alkali can also be called a base.)

Acids have H⁺ ions   Alkalis have OH⁻ ions

The strict definitions of acids and alkalis are:

> *ACIDS* are substances which form $H^+_{(aq)}$ *ions* when added to *water*.
>
> *ALKALIS* are substances which form $OH^-_{(aq)}$ *ions* when added to *water*.

Neutralisation

This is the equation for any neutralisation reaction. Make sure you learn it:

$$Acid + alkali \rightarrow salt + water$$

Neutralisation can also be seen in terms of ions like this, so learn it too:

$$H^+_{(aq)} + OH^-_{(aq)} \rightarrow H_2O_{(l)}$$

Three "Real life" Examples of Neutralisation:

1) Indigestion is caused by too much hydrochloric acid in the stomach.
   Indigestion tablets contain alkalis such as magnesium oxide, which neutralise the excess HCl.

2) Fields with acidic soils can be improved no end by adding lime (See P. 23).
   The lime added to fields is calcium hydroxide $Ca(OH)_2$ which is of course an alkali.

3) Lakes affected by acid rain can also be neutralised by adding lime. This saves the fish.

Hey man, like "acid", yeah — eeuuucch...

Try and enjoy this page on acids and alkalis, because it gets really tedious from now on. These are very basic facts and possibly quite interesting. Cover the page and scribble them down.

Acids Reacting With Metals

Acid + Metal → Salt + Hydrogen

That's written big 'cos it's kinda worth remembering. Here's the _typical experiment_:

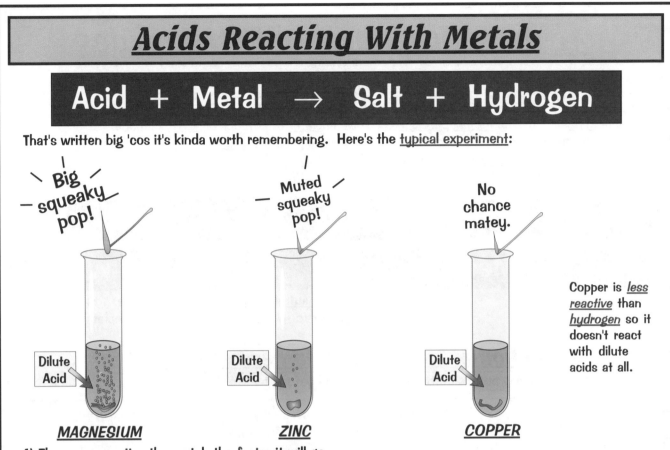

| Big squeaky pop! | Muted squeaky pop! | No chance matey. |

Copper is _less reactive_ than _hydrogen_ so it doesn't react with dilute acids at all.

MAGNESIUM **ZINC** **COPPER**

1) The _more reactive_ the metal, the _faster_ it will go.

2) _Copper_ does _not_ react with dilute acids _at all_ — because it's _less reactive than hydrogen_.

3) The _speed of reaction_ is indicated by the _rate_ at which the _bubbles of hydrogen_ are given off.

4) The _hydrogen_ is confirmed by the _burning splint test_ giving the notorious "_squeaky pop_".

5) The _type of salt_ produced depends on which _metal_ is used, and which _acid_ is used:

Hydrochloric acid _will always produce_ chloride _salts:_

$$2HCl + Mg \rightarrow MgCl_2 + H_2 \quad \text{(Magnesium chloride)}$$

$$2HCl + Zn \rightarrow ZnCl_2 + H_2 \quad \text{(Zinc chloride)}$$

Sulphuric acid _will always produce_ sulphate _salts:_

$$H_2SO_4 + Mg \rightarrow MgSO_4 + H_2 \quad \text{(Magnesium sulphate)}$$

$$H_2SO_4 + Zn \rightarrow ZnSO_4 + H_2 \quad \text{(Zinc sulphate)}$$

Nitric acid _produces_ nitrate _salts when_ NEUTRALISED, but...

Nitric acid reacts fine with alkalis, to produce nitrates, but it can play silly devils with metals and produce nitrogen oxides instead, so we'll ignore it here. Chemistry's a real messy subject sometimes, innit.

Revision of Acids and Metals — easy as squeaky pop...

Actually, this stuff isn't too bad I don't think. I mean it's fairly interesting. Not quite in the same league as base jumping, I grant you, but for Chemistry it's not bad at all. At least there's bubbles and flames and noise and that kinda thing. Anyway, _learn it, scribble it down, etc_...

Acids with Oxides and Hydroxides

Metal Oxides and Metal Hydroxides are Alkalis

1) Some metal oxides and metal hydroxides dissolve in water to produce alkaline solutions.
2) In other words, metal oxides and metal hydroxides are generally alkalis.
3) This means they'll react with acids to form a salt and water.
4) Even those that won't dissolve in water will still react with acid.

Acid + Metal Oxide → Salt + Water

Acid + Metal Hydroxide → Salt + Water

(These are neutralisation reactions of course. You can use an indicator to tell when they've reacted completely.)

The Combination of Metal and Acid decides the Salt

This isn't exactly exciting but it's pretty easy, so try and get the hang of it:

Hydrochloric acid	+ Copper oxide	→	Copper chloride	+ water
Hydrochloric acid	+ Sodium hydroxide	→	Sodium chloride	+ water
Sulphuric acid	+ Zinc oxide	→	Zinc sulphate	+ water
Sulphuric acid	+ Calcium hydroxide	→	Calcium sulphate	+ water
Nitric acid	+ Magnesium oxide	→	Magnesium nitrate	+ water
Nitric acid	+ Potassium hydroxide	→	Potassium nitrate	+ water

The symbol equations are all pretty much the same. Here's two of them:

$$H_2SO_4 + ZnO \rightarrow ZnSO_4 + H_2O$$

$$HNO_3 + KOH \rightarrow KNO_3 + H_2O$$

The Oxides of non-metals are usually Acidic, not alkaline

1) The best examples are the oxides of these three non-metals: carbon, sulphur and nitrogen.
2) Carbon dioxide dissolves in water to form carbonic acid which is a weak acid.
3) Sulphur Dioxide combines with water and O_2 to form sulphuric acid which is a strong acid.
4) Nitrogen dioxide dissolves in water to form nitric acid which is a strong acid.
5) These three are all present in acid rain of course.
6) The carbonic acid is present in rain anyway, so even ordinary rain is slightly acidic.
   Remember the three examples:

Non-metal oxides are acidic:
Carbon dioxide   Sulphur dioxide   Nitrogen dioxide

Acids are really dull, aren't they — learn and snore...

You've gotta be a pretty serious career chemist to find this stuff interesting.
Normal people (like you and me!) just have to grin and bear it. Oh, and learn it as well, of course
— don't forget the small matter of those little Exams you've got coming up... remember?

Acids With Carbonates and Ammonia

More gripping reactions involving acids. At least there's some bubbles involved here.

Acid + Carbonate → Salt + Water + Carbon dioxide

Acid + Hydrogencarbonate → Salt + Water + Carbon dioxide

1) <u>Definitely</u> learn the fact that <u>carbonates</u> and <u>hydrogencarbonates</u> give off <u>carbon dioxide</u>.
2) If you also <u>practise</u> writing the following equations out <u>from memory</u>, it'll do you no harm at all.

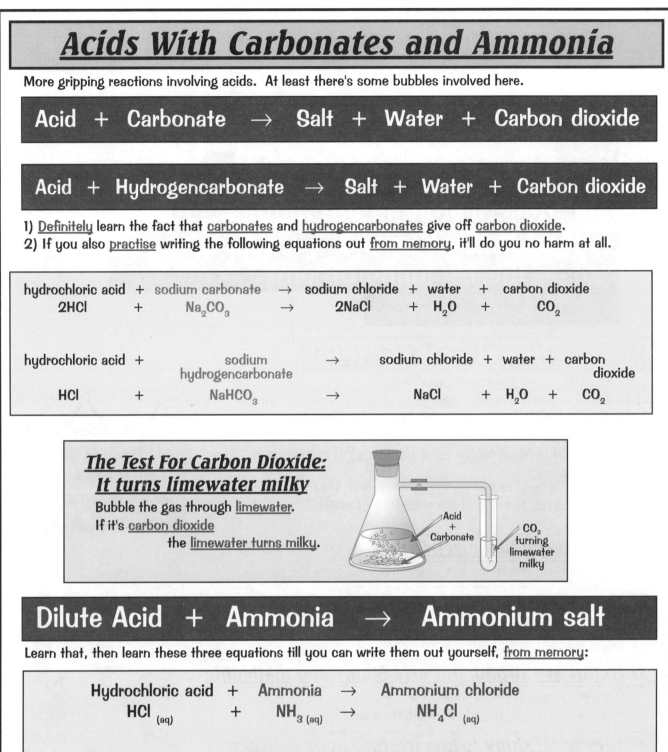

hydrochloric acid + sodium carbonate → sodium chloride + water + carbon dioxide
$$2HCl + Na_2CO_3 \rightarrow 2NaCl + H_2O + CO_2$$

hydrochloric acid + sodium hydrogencarbonate → sodium chloride + water + carbon dioxide
$$HCl + NaHCO_3 \rightarrow NaCl + H_2O + CO_2$$

The Test For Carbon Dioxide:
It turns limewater milky

Bubble the gas through <u>limewater</u>.
If it's <u>carbon dioxide</u>
    the <u>limewater turns milky</u>.

Acid + Carbonate

CO_2 turning limewater milky

Dilute Acid + Ammonia → Ammonium salt

Learn that, then learn these three equations till you can write them out yourself, <u>from memory</u>:

Hydrochloric acid + Ammonia → Ammonium chloride
$$HCl_{(aq)} + NH_{3\,(aq)} \rightarrow NH_4Cl_{(aq)}$$

Sulphuric acid + Ammonia → Ammonium sulphate
$$H_2SO_{4\,(aq)} + 2NH_{3\,(aq)} \rightarrow (NH_4)_2SO_{4\,(aq)}$$

Nitric acid + Ammonia → Ammonium nitrate
$$HNO_{3\,(aq)} + NH_{3\,(aq)} \rightarrow NH_4NO_{3\,(aq)}$$

This last reaction with nitric acid produces the famous <u>ammonium nitrate</u> fertiliser, much appreciated for its <u>double dose</u> of essential nitrogen. (See P. 25)

Still Awake, eh? — learning this page should finish you off...

Phew, the last page on acids, thank goodness. <u>Learn</u> the last of these dreary facts and try to <u>scribble it down</u>. (If there's an Acid Appreciation Action Group, they're sure gonna be after me.)

Metals

All these elements are metals
Just look at 'em all
— there's loads of 'em!

The Metallic Crystal Structure

1) <u>All</u> metals have the <u>same</u> basic properties.
2) These are due to the <u>special type of bonding</u> that exists in metals.
3) Metals consist of a <u>giant structure</u> of atoms held together with <u>metallic bonds</u>.
4) These special bonds allow the <u>outer electron(s)</u> of each atom to <u>move freely</u>.
5) This creates a "<u>sea</u>" of <u>free electrons</u> throughout the metal which is what gives rise to many of the properties of metals.

Metal atoms   Free electrons

1) They all conduct electricity
This is entirely due to the <u>free electrons</u> which <u>carry the current</u>.

2) They're all good conductors of heat
Again this is entirely due to the <u>free electrons</u> which <u>carry the heat energy</u> through the metal.

3) Metals are strong, but also bendy and malleable
They are <u>strong</u> (hard to break), but they can be <u>bent or hammered</u> into a different shape.

Don't try this at home. You'll die.

4) They're all shiny (when freshly cut or polished)

5) They have high melting and boiling points
Which means you have to get them <u>pretty hot</u> to <u>melt them</u> (except good old mercury). e.g. copper 1100°C, tungsten 3377°C

6) They can be mixed together to form many useful alloys:

1) <u>Steel</u> is an <u>alloy</u> (mixture) of <u>iron</u> and about <u>1% carbon</u>. Steel is much <u>less brittle</u> than iron.
2) <u>Bronze</u> is an <u>alloy</u> of <u>copper</u> and <u>tin</u>. It's harder than copper but still easily shaped.
3) <u>Copper</u> and <u>nickel</u> (75%:25%) are used to make <u>cupro-nickel</u> which is hard enough for <u>coins</u>.

Metal Fatigue? — yeah, we've all had enough of this page now...
Phew.

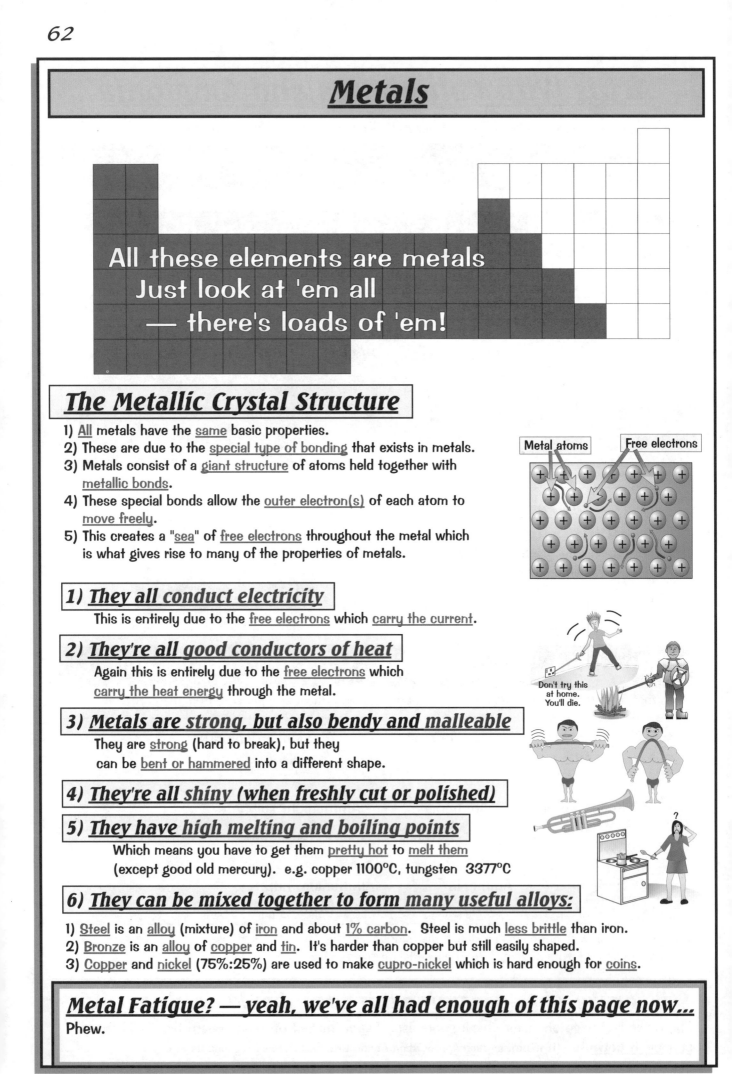

Non-Metals

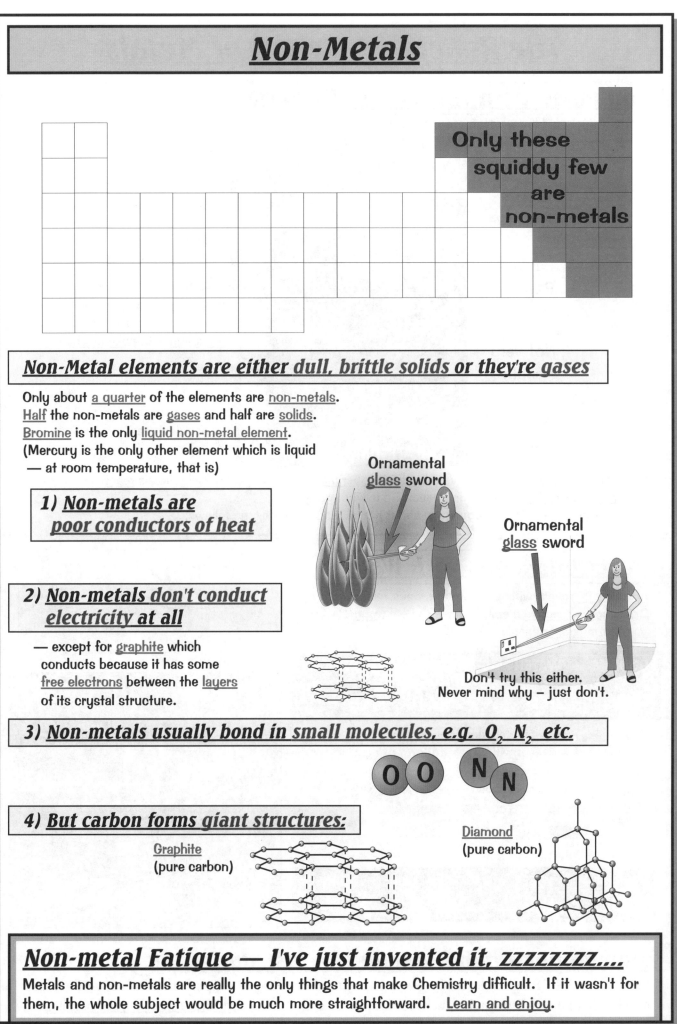

Only these squiddy few are non-metals

Non-Metal elements are either dull, brittle solids or they're gases

Only about <u>a quarter</u> of the elements are <u>non-metals</u>.
<u>Half</u> the non-metals are <u>gases</u> and half are <u>solids</u>.
<u>Bromine</u> is the only <u>liquid non-metal element</u>.
(Mercury is the only other element which is liquid
— at room temperature, that is)

1) Non-metals are poor conductors of heat

Ornamental <u>glass</u> sword

Ornamental <u>glass</u> sword

2) Non-metals don't conduct electricity at all

— except for <u>graphite</u> which conducts because it has some <u>free electrons</u> between the <u>layers</u> of its crystal structure.

Don't try this either.
Never mind why – just don't.

3) Non-metals usually bond in small molecules, e.g. O_2 N_2 etc.

O O N N

4) But carbon forms giant structures:

Graphite
(pure carbon)

Diamond
(pure carbon)

Non-metal Fatigue — I've just invented it, zzzzzzzz....

Metals and non-metals are really the only things that make Chemistry difficult. If it wasn't for them, the whole subject would be much more straightforward. <u>Learn and enjoy</u>.

The Reactivity Series of Metals

You must learn this Reactivity Series

You really should know which are the more reactive metals and which are the less reactive ones.

THE REACTIVITY SERIES

Very Reactive	POTASSIUM	K
	SODIUM	Na
	CALCIUM	Ca
Fairly Reactive	MAGNESIUM	Mg
	ALUMINIUM	Al
	(CARBON)	
	ZINC	Zn
Not very Reactive	IRON	Fe
	LEAD	Pb
	(HYDROGEN)	
	COPPER	Cu
Not at all Reactive	SILVER	Ag
	GOLD	Au
	PLATINUM	Pt

Metals <u>above carbon</u> must be extracted from their ores by <u>electrolysis</u>.

Metals <u>below carbon</u> can be extracted from their ore using <u>reduction</u> with <u>coke or charcoal</u>.

Metals <u>below hydrogen</u> don't react with <u>water</u> or <u>acid</u>. They don't easily <u>tarnish</u> or <u>corrode</u>.

This <u>reactivity series</u> was determined by doing <u>experiments</u> to see <u>how strongly</u> metals <u>react</u>. The <u>standard reaction</u> to determine reactivity is with <u>water</u>. It's <u>important</u> so make sure you know about it in reasonable detail, as follows:

Reacting Metals With Water

1) If a <u>metal</u> reacts with <u>water</u> it will always release <u>hydrogen</u>.
2) The <u>more reactive</u> metals react with <u>cold water</u> to form <u>hydroxides</u>:

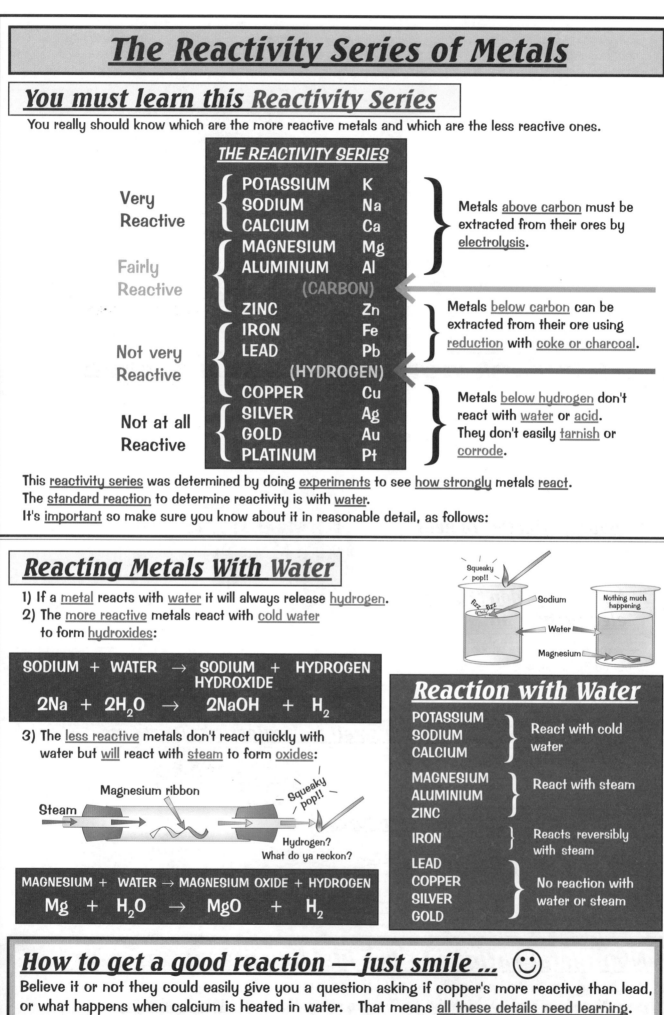
Squeaky pop!!
Sodium
Water
Magnesium
Nothing much happening

SODIUM + WATER → SODIUM HYDROXIDE + HYDROGEN

$$2Na + 2H_2O \rightarrow 2NaOH + H_2$$

3) The <u>less reactive</u> metals don't react quickly with water but <u>will</u> react with <u>steam</u> to form <u>oxides</u>:

Magnesium ribbon
Steam
Squeaky pop!!
Hydrogen? What do ya reckon?

MAGNESIUM + WATER → MAGNESIUM OXIDE + HYDROGEN

$$Mg + H_2O \rightarrow MgO + H_2$$

Reaction with Water

POTASSIUM SODIUM CALCIUM	React with cold water
MAGNESIUM ALUMINIUM ZINC	React with steam
IRON	Reacts reversibly with steam
LEAD COPPER SILVER GOLD	No reaction with water or steam

How to get a good reaction — just smile ... ☺

Believe it or not they could easily give you a question asking if copper's more reactive than lead, or what happens when calcium is heated in water. That means <u>all these details need learning</u>.

Transition Metals

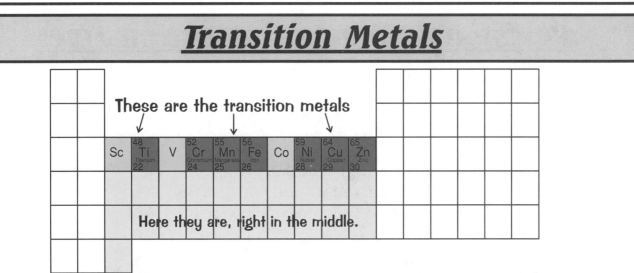

These are the transition metals

Here they are, right in the middle.

Titanium, Chromium, Manganese, Iron, Nickel, Copper, Zinc

You need to know the ones shown in red fairly well. If they wanted to be mean in the Exam _(if!)_ they could cheerfully mention one of the others like scandium or cobalt or vanadium.

Don't let it hassle you. They'll just be testing how well you can _"apply scientific knowledge to new information"_. In other words, just assume these "new" transition metals follow all the properties you've already learnt for the others. That's all it is, but it can really worry some folk.

Transition Metals all have high melting point and high density

They're <u>typical metals</u>. They have the properties you would expect of a proper metal:

1) <u>Good conductors</u> of heat and electricity. They're very <u>dense</u>, <u>strong</u> and <u>shiny</u>.

2) Iron melts at 1500°C, copper melts at 1100°C and zinc melts at 400°C.

Transition Metals and their compounds all make good catalysts

1) <u>Iron</u> is the <u>catalyst</u> used in the <u>Haber process</u> for making <u>ammonia</u>.

2) <u>Manganese(IV) oxide</u> is a good <u>catalyst</u> for the decomposition of <u>hydrogen peroxide</u>.

3) <u>Nickel</u> is useful for turning <u>oils into fats</u> for making margarine.

The compounds are very colourful

1) The <u>compounds</u> are <u>colourful</u> due to the <u>transition metal ion</u> they contain. e.g. <u>Potassium chromate(VI)</u> is yellow. <u>Potassium manganate(VII)</u> is purple. <u>Copper(II) sulphate</u> is blue.

2) The colour of people's <u>hair</u> and also the colours in <u>gemstones</u>, like <u>blue sapphires</u> and <u>green emeralds</u>, and the colours in <u>pottery glazes</u> are all due to <u>transition metals</u>.
...And weathered (oxidised) <u>copper</u> is a lovely colourful <u>green</u>.

Transition Metals often have more than one ion, e.g. Fe^{2+}, Fe^{3+}

Two other examples are <u>copper</u>: Cu^+ and Cu^{2+} and <u>chromium</u>: Cr^{2+} and Cr^{3+}

The <u>different ions</u> usually have <u>different colours</u> too:

Fe^{2+} ions usually give <u>green</u> compounds, whereas Fe^{3+} ions are usually <u>red/brown</u> (rust!)

Uses of Iron, Copper, Zinc and Titanium

1) <u>Iron</u> is used for <u>man-hole covers</u>. <u>Pure iron</u> is very <u>brittle</u>, unlike steel which is more useful.

2) <u>Copper</u> is used for <u>electric wiring</u> and household <u>water pipes</u>. Copper and <u>nickel</u> make <u>coins</u>.

3) <u>Zinc</u> is used for <u>galvanising</u> iron. <u>Zinc</u> and <u>copper</u> make the alloy <u>brass</u> for trumpets and tubas.

4) <u>Titanium</u> is used to make <u>strong</u>, <u>light</u> alloys for aircraft and missiles.

Lots of pretty colours — that's what we like to see...

There's quite a few things to learn about transition metals. First try to remember the six headings. Then learn the details that go under each one. <u>Keep trying to scribble it all down.</u>

Revision Summary for Section Five

Phew, I tell you what you know — there's some serious Chemistry in Section Five.
I suppose it makes up for Section Four being so easy. This is where all the really grisly stuff is.
All I can say is, just keep trying to learn it. These jolly questions will give you some idea of how well
you're doing. For any you can't do, you'll find the answers somewhere in Section Five.

1) What two properties did they base the early periodic table on?

2) Who was the old rogue who had the best shot at it and why was his table so clever?

3) What feature of atoms determines the order of the modern Periodic Table?

4) What are the Periods and Groups? Explain their significance in terms of electrons.

5) Draw diagrams to show the electron arrangements for the first twenty elements.

6) Explain the trend in reactivity of metals and non-metals using the notion of "shielding".

7) What are the electron arrangements of the noble gases? What are the properties of them?

8) Give two uses each for helium, neon and argon.

9) Which Group are the alkali metals? What is their outer shell like?

10) List four physical properties, and two chemical properties of the alkali metals.

11) Give details of the reactions of the alkali metals with water.

12) What can you say about the pH of alkali metal oxides and hydroxides?

13) Describe the trends in appearance and reactivity of the halogens as you go down the Group.

14) List four properties common to all the halogens.

15) Give details, with equations, of the reaction of the halogens with metals.

16) Give details, with equations, of the displacement reactions of the halogens.

17) What is hydrogen chloride? Exactly how do you produce an acid solution from it?

18) What are the two sources of salt and what are the three main uses of it?

19) Draw a full diagram of the electrolysis of salt and list the three useful products it creates.

20) Give a use for each of the four halogens: fluorine, chlorine, bromine and iodine.

21) Give uses for the three products from the electrolysis of brine.

22) Describe fully the colour of universal indicator for every pH value from 1 to 14.

23) What type of ions are always present in a) acids and   b) alkalis? What is neutralisation?

24) What is the equation for reacting acid with metal? Which metal(s) don't react with acid?

25) What type of salts do hydrochloric acid and sulphuric acid produce?

26) What type of reaction is "acid + metal oxide", or "acid + metal hydroxide"?

27) What about the oxides of non-metals — are they acidic or alkaline?

28) What are the equations for reacting acids with carbonates and hydrogencarbonates?

29) What is the equation for reacting dilute acid with ammonia?

30) What proportion of the elements are metals? What do all metals contain?

31) List six properties of metals. List four properties of non-metals.

32) Write down the twelve common metals in the order of the Reactivity Series.

33) Where do carbon and hydrogen fit in and what is the significance of their positions?

34) Describe the reaction of all twelve metals with water (or steam).

35) List four properties of transition metals, and two properties of their compounds.

36) Name six transition metals, and give uses for three of them.

Rates of Reaction

Reactions can go at all sorts of different rates

1) One of the <u>slowest</u> is the <u>rusting</u> of iron (it's not slow enough though — what about my little MGB).
2) Other slow reactions include <u>chemical weathering</u>, like acid rain damage to limestone buildings.
3) A <u>moderate speed</u> reaction is a <u>metal</u> (like magnesium) reacting with <u>acid</u> to produce a <u>gentle stream of bubbles</u>.
4) A <u>really fast</u> reaction is an <u>explosion</u>, where it's all over in a <u>fraction of a second</u>.

Three ways to Measure the Speed of a Reaction

The <u>speed of reaction</u> can be observed <u>either</u> by how quickly the <u>reactants are used up</u> or how quickly the <u>products are forming</u>. It's usually a lot easier to measure <u>products forming</u>.
There are <u>three different ways</u> that the speed of a reaction can be <u>measured</u>:

1) Precipitation

This is when the <u>product</u> of the reaction is a <u>precipitate</u> which <u>clouds the solution</u>. Observe a <u>marker</u> through the solution and measure <u>how long it takes</u> for it to <u>disappear</u>.

2) Change in mass (usually gas given off)

Any reaction that <u>produces a gas</u> can be carried out on a <u>mass balance</u> and as the gas is released the mass <u>disappearing</u> is easily measured.

3) The volume of gas given off

This involves the use of a <u>gas syringe</u> to measure the volume of gas given off. But that's about all there is to it.

The Rate of a Reaction Depends on Four Things:

1) <u>TEMPERATURE</u>
2) <u>CONCENTRATION</u>   — (or <u>PRESSURE</u> for gases)
3) <u>CATALYST</u>
4) <u>SIZE OF PARTICLES</u>   — (or <u>SURFACE AREA</u>)

LEARN THEM!

Typical Graphs for Rate of Reaction

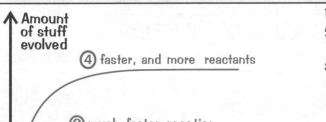

④ faster, and more reactants

③ much faster reaction

② faster reaction

① original reaction

Amount of stuff evolved

Time

1) <u>Graph 1</u> represents the original <u>fairly slow</u> reaction.
2) <u>Graphs 2 and 3</u> represent the reaction taking place <u>quicker</u> but with the <u>same initial amounts</u>.
3) The <u>increased rate</u> could be due to <u>any</u> of these:

   a) increase in <u>temperature</u>
   b) increase in <u>concentration</u> (or pressure)
   c) solid reactant crushed up into <u>smaller bits</u>
   d) <u>catalyst</u> added.

4) <u>Graph 4</u> produces <u>more product</u> as well as going <u>quicker</u>. This can <u>only</u> happen if <u>more reactant(s)</u> are added at the start.

How to get a fast, furious reaction — crack a wee joke...

There's all sorts of bits and bobs of information on this page. To learn it all, you've got to learn to split it up into separate sections and do them one at a time. Practise by <u>covering the page</u> and seeing how much you can <u>scribble down</u> for each section. <u>Then try again, and again...</u>

Collision Theory

Reaction rates are explained perfectly by Collision Theory. It's really simple.
It just says that the rate of a reaction simply depends on how often and how hard
the reacting particles collide with each other. The basic idea is that particles have
to collide in order to react, and they have to collide hard enough as well.

More Collisions increases the Rate of Reaction

All the methods of increasing the rate of reactions can be explained in terms of
increasing the number of collisions between the reacting particles;

1) TEMPERATURE increases the number of collisions

When the temperature is increased the particles all move quicker.
If they're moving quicker, they're going to have more collisions.

Cold   Hot

2) CONCENTRATION (or PRESSURE) increases the number of collisions

If the solution is made more concentrated it means there are more
particles of reactant knocking about between the water molecules
which makes collisions between the important particles more likely.
In a gas, increasing the pressure means the molecules are more
squashed up together so there are going to be more collisions.

Low Concentration   High Concentration
(Low Pressure)   (High Pressure)

3) SIZE OF SOLID PARTICLES (or SURFACE AREA) increases collisions

If one of the reactants is a solid then breaking it up into
smaller pieces will increase its surface area. This means
the particles around it in the solution will have more area
to work on so there'll be more useful collisions.

4) CATALYST increases the number of collisions

A catalyst works by giving the reacting
particles a surface to stick to where they can
bump into each other. This obviously
increases the number of collisions too.

Surface of catalyst

Faster Collisions increase the Rate of Reaction

Higher temperature also increases the energy of the collisions, because it makes all the particles move faster.

Faster collisions are ONLY caused by increasing the temperature

Reactions only happen if the particles collide with enough
energy. At a higher temperature there will be more particles
colliding with enough energy to make the reaction happen.
This initial energy is known as the activation energy, and it's
needed to break the initial bonds. (See P. 79)

Cool Atoms   Hot Atoms

Collision Theory — it's always the other driver...

This is quite easy I think. Isn't it all kind of obvious — at least once you've been told it, anyway.
The more often particles collide and the harder they hit, the greater the reaction rate. There's a
few extra picky details of course (isn't there always!), but you've only got to LEARN them...

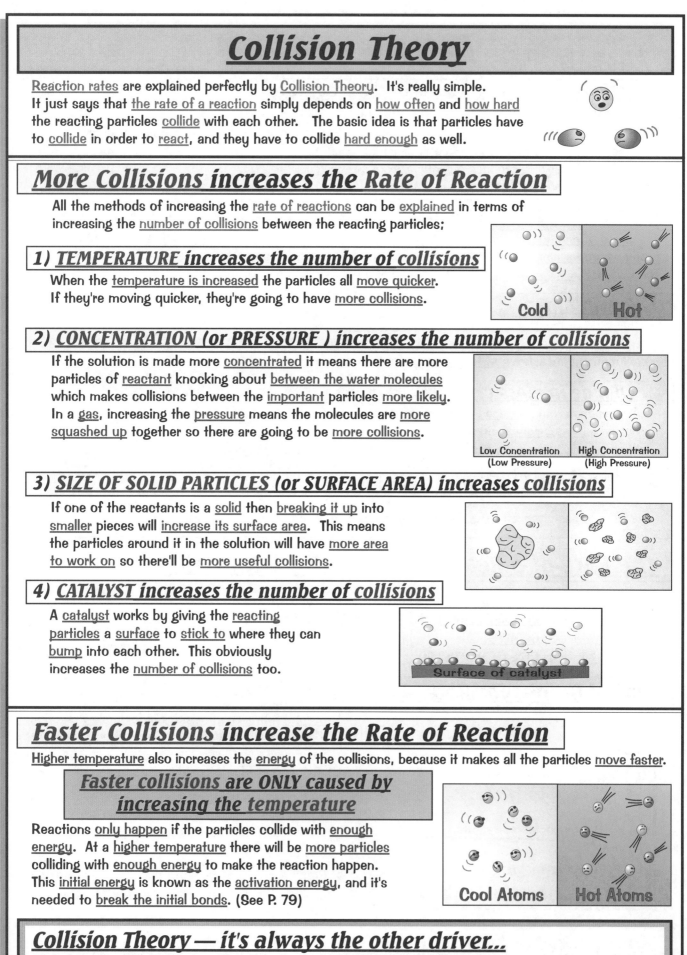

Four Experiments on Rate of Reaction 1

<u>REMEMBER:</u> <u>Any reaction</u> can be used to investigate <u>any of the four factors</u> that affect the <u>rate</u>.
These pages illustrate <u>four important reactions</u>, but only <u>one factor</u> has been considered for each.
But we could <u>just as easily</u> use, say, the marble chips/acid reaction to test the effect of <u>temperature</u> instead.

1) Reaction of Hydrochloric Acid and Marble Chips

This experiment is often used to demonstrate the effect of <u>breaking the solid up</u> into <u>small bits</u>.

1) Measure the <u>volume</u> of gas evolved with a <u>gas syringe</u> and take readings at <u>regular intervals</u>.
2) Make a <u>table of readings</u> and plot them as a <u>graph</u>.
3) <u>Repeat</u> the experiment with <u>exactly the same</u> volume of <u>acid</u>, and <u>exactly the same</u> mass of <u>marble</u> chips, but with the marble <u>more crunched up</u>.
4) Then <u>repeat</u> with the same mass of <u>powdered chalk</u> instead of marble chips.

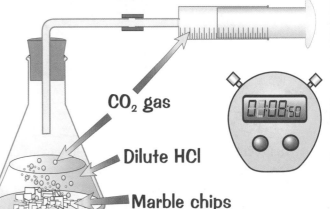

CO$_2$ gas

Dilute HCl

Marble chips

These graphs show the effect of using finer particles of solid

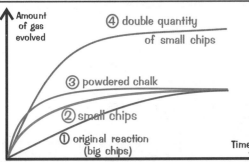

④ double quantity of small chips
③ powdered chalk
② small chips
① original reaction (big chips)
Amount of gas evolved
Time

1) The increase in <u>surface area</u> causes <u>more collisions</u> so the rate of reaction is <u>faster</u>.
2) <u>Graph 4</u> shows the reaction if a <u>greater mass</u> of small marble chips is added.
3) The <u>extra surface area</u> gives a <u>quicker reaction</u> and there is also <u>more gas evolved</u> overall.

2) Reaction of Magnesium Metal With Dilute HCl

1) <u>This reaction</u> is good for measuring the effects of <u>increased concentration</u>, (as is the marble/acid reaction).

2) This reaction gives off <u>hydrogen gas</u>, which we can measure with a <u>mass balance</u>, as shown.
(The other method is to use a gas syringe, as above.)

These graphs show the effect of using stronger acid solutions

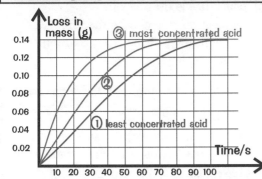

Loss in mass (g)
③ most concentrated acid
②
① least concentrated acid
Time/s
10 20 30 40 50 60 70 80 90 100

1) Take <u>readings of the mass</u> at <u>regular</u> time intervals.
2) Put the results in a <u>table</u> and <u>work out</u> the <u>loss in mass</u> for each reading. <u>Plot a graph</u>.
3) <u>Repeat</u> with <u>stronger acid solutions</u> but always with the <u>same amount of magnesium</u>.
4) The <u>volume</u> of acid must always be kept <u>the same</u> too — only the <u>concentration</u> is increased.
5) The three graphs show <u>the same old pattern</u>. <u>Higher</u> concentration giving a <u>steeper graph</u> with the reaction <u>finishing</u> much quicker.

Section Six — Reaction Rates

Four Experiments on Rate of Reaction 2

3) Sodium Thiosulphate and HCl produce a Cloudy Precipitate

1) These two chemicals are both <u>clear solutions</u>.
2) They react together to form a <u>yellow precipitate</u> of <u>sulphur</u>.
3) <u>The experiment</u> involves watching a black mark <u>disappear</u> through the <u>cloudy sulphur</u> and <u>timing</u> how long it takes to go.

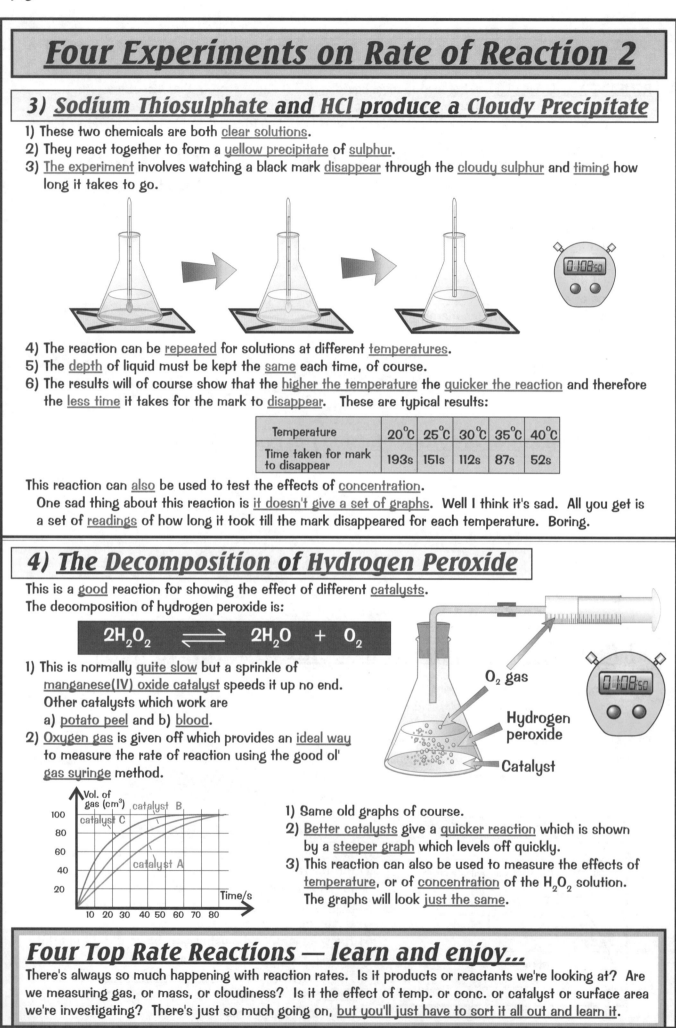

4) The reaction can be <u>repeated</u> for solutions at different <u>temperatures</u>.
5) The <u>depth</u> of liquid must be kept the <u>same</u> each time, of course.
6) The results will of course show that the <u>higher the temperature</u> the <u>quicker the reaction</u> and therefore the <u>less time</u> it takes for the mark to <u>disappear</u>. These are typical results:

Temperature	20°C	25°C	30°C	35°C	40°C
Time taken for mark to disappear	193s	151s	112s	87s	52s

This reaction can <u>also</u> be used to test the effects of <u>concentration</u>.
   One sad thing about this reaction is <u>it doesn't give a set of graphs</u>. Well I think it's sad. All you get is a set of <u>readings</u> of how long it took till the mark disappeared for each temperature. Boring.

4) The Decomposition of Hydrogen Peroxide

This is a <u>good</u> reaction for showing the effect of different <u>catalysts</u>.
The decomposition of hydrogen peroxide is:

$$2H_2O_2 \rightleftharpoons 2H_2O + O_2$$

1) This is normally <u>quite slow</u> but a sprinkle of <u>manganese(IV) oxide catalyst</u> speeds it up no end. Other catalysts which work are
a) <u>potato peel</u> and b) <u>blood</u>.
2) <u>Oxygen gas</u> is given off which provides an <u>ideal way</u> to measure the rate of reaction using the good ol' <u>gas syringe</u> method.

O_2 gas

Hydrogen peroxide

Catalyst

1) Same old graphs of course.
2) <u>Better catalysts</u> give a <u>quicker reaction</u> which is shown by a <u>steeper graph</u> which levels off quickly.
3) This reaction can also be used to measure the effects of <u>temperature</u>, or of <u>concentration</u> of the H_2O_2 solution. The graphs will look <u>just the same</u>.

Four Top Rate Reactions — learn and enjoy...

There's always so much happening with reaction rates. Is it products or reactants we're looking at? Are we measuring gas, or mass, or cloudiness? Is it the effect of temp. or conc. or catalyst or surface area we're investigating? There's just so much going on, <u>but you'll just have to sort it all out and learn it</u>.

Catalysts

Many reactions can be <u>speeded up</u> by adding a <u>catalyst</u>.

> A <u>***CATALYST***</u> is a substance which <u>***INCREASES***</u> the speed of a reaction, without being <u>***CHANGED***</u> or <u>***USED UP***</u> in the reaction.

1) Catalysts lower the Activation Energy

1) Catalysts <u>lower</u> the <u>activation energy</u> (see P. 79) of reactions, making it <u>easier</u> for them to happen.
2) This means a <u>lower temperature</u> can be used.

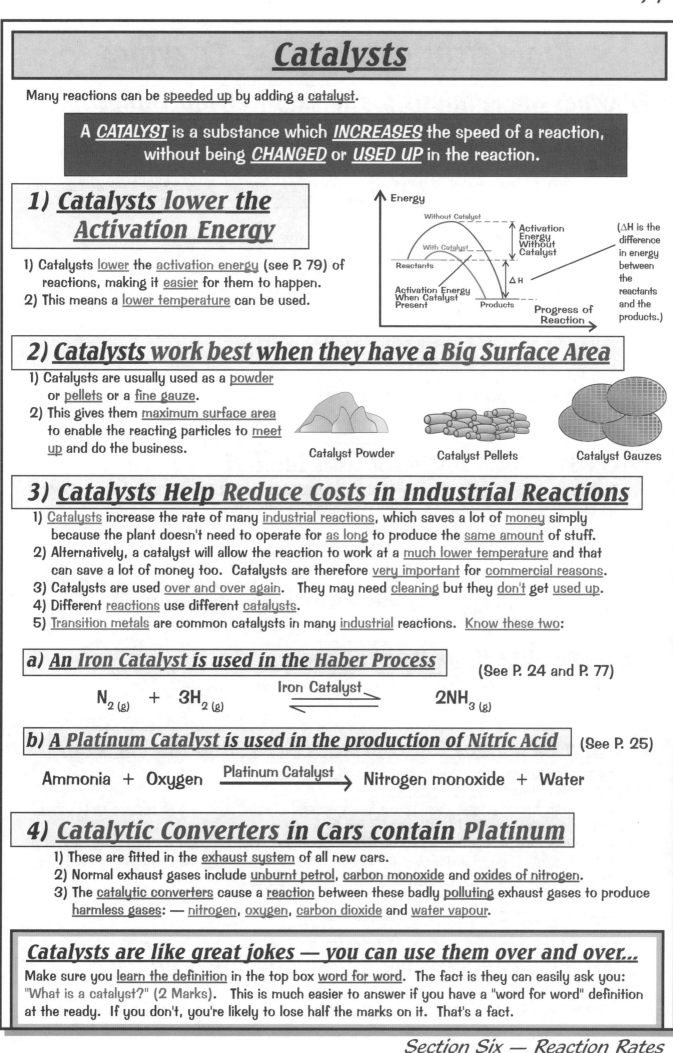

Energy

Without Catalyst

With Catalyst

Reactants

Activation Energy When Catalyst Present

Activation Energy Without Catalyst

ΔH

Products

Progress of Reaction

(ΔH is the difference in energy between the reactants and the products.)

2) Catalysts work best when they have a Big Surface Area

1) Catalysts are usually used as a <u>powder</u> or <u>pellets</u> or a <u>fine gauze</u>.
2) This gives them <u>maximum surface area</u> to enable the reacting particles to <u>meet up</u> and do the business.

Catalyst Powder   Catalyst Pellets   Catalyst Gauzes

3) Catalysts Help Reduce Costs in Industrial Reactions

1) <u>Catalysts</u> increase the rate of many <u>industrial reactions</u>, which saves a lot of <u>money</u> simply because the plant doesn't need to operate for <u>as long</u> to produce the <u>same amount</u> of stuff.
2) Alternatively, a catalyst will allow the reaction to work at a <u>much lower temperature</u> and that can save a lot of money too. Catalysts are therefore <u>very important</u> for <u>commercial reasons</u>.
3) Catalysts are used <u>over and over again</u>. They may need <u>cleaning</u> but they <u>don't</u> get <u>used up</u>.
4) Different <u>reactions</u> use different <u>catalysts</u>.
5) <u>Transition metals</u> are common catalysts in many <u>industrial</u> reactions. <u>Know these two</u>:

a) An Iron Catalyst is used in the Haber Process (See P. 24 and P. 77)

$$N_{2(g)} \; + \; 3H_{2(g)} \; \xrightleftharpoons{\text{Iron Catalyst}} \; 2NH_{3(g)}$$

b) A Platinum Catalyst is used in the production of Nitric Acid (See P. 25)

$$\text{Ammonia} + \text{Oxygen} \xrightarrow{\text{Platinum Catalyst}} \text{Nitrogen monoxide} + \text{Water}$$

4) Catalytic Converters in Cars contain Platinum

1) These are fitted in the <u>exhaust system</u> of all new cars.
2) Normal exhaust gases include <u>unburnt petrol</u>, <u>carbon monoxide</u> and <u>oxides of nitrogen</u>.
3) The <u>catalytic converters</u> cause a <u>reaction</u> between these badly <u>polluting</u> exhaust gases to produce <u>harmless gases</u>: — <u>nitrogen</u>, <u>oxygen</u>, <u>carbon dioxide</u> and <u>water vapour</u>.

Catalysts are like great jokes — you can use them over and over...

Make sure you <u>learn the definition</u> in the top box <u>word for word</u>. The fact is they can easily ask you: "What is a catalyst?" (2 Marks). This is much easier to answer if you have a "word for word" definition at the ready. If you don't, you're likely to lose half the marks on it. That's a fact.

Biological Catalysts — Enzymes

Enzymes are Catalysts produced by Living Things

1) Living things have thousands of different chemical processes going on inside them.
2) The quicker these happen the better, and raising the temperature of the body is an important way to speed them up.
3) However, there's a limit to how far you can raise the temperature before cells start getting damaged, so living things also produce enzymes which act as catalysts to speed up all these chemical reactions without the need for high temperatures.
4) Enzymes themselves only perform well within a fairly narrow range of temperature.
5) Every different biological process has its own enzyme designed especially for it.
6) For example the way an apple turns brown when cut is caused by a particular enzyme.
7) Humans are now starting to use biological catalysts more and more for their own purposes.
8) Enzymes have many advantages over traditional non-organic catalysts:
    a) There's a huge variety of enzymes.
    b) They're not scarce like many metal catalysts e.g. platinum.
    c) They work best at low temperatures and pressures, which keeps costs down.
    d) They can be carefully selected to do a precise job.
EXAMPLES: "biological" washing powders, dishwasher powders, and in the treatment of leather.

Enzymes Like it Warm but Not Too Hot

Enzyme Activity

This is the optimum temperature — where the enzyme is most active.

Temp.

0°C   45°C

1) The chemical reactions in living cells are quite fast in conditions that are warm rather than hot.
2) This is because the cells use catalysts called enzymes, which are protein molecules.
3) Enzymes are usually damaged by temperatures above about 45°C, and as the graph shows, their activity drops off sharply when the temperature gets a little too high.

Enzymes Like it the Right pH too

The pH affects the activity of enzymes, in a similar way to temperature.

Enzyme Activity

Optimum pH

pH

Freezing food stops the enzyme activity (and the bacteria)

1) At lower temperatures, enzyme activity also drops quite quickly.
2) By 0°C there's virtually nothing happening.
3) This is the idea behind refrigeration, where foods are kept at about 4°C to keep enzyme and bacterial activity to a minimum so that food stays fresher for longer.
4) Freezers store food at about -20°C and at this temperature bacteria and enzymes don't function at all.
5) However, they're not destroyed by freezing and once the food thaws out they spring back into action. So frozen food should be thawed carefully and then cooked again before eating.
6) Cooking destroys all bacteria and enzymes, so properly cooked food is safe to eat.
7) However, even cooked foods will go off pretty rapidly if left in a warm place.

"Enzymes" — sounds like a brand of throat lozenge...

This page is definitely a candidate for the mini-essay method. Two mini-essays in fact. What else is there to say? Scribble down the facts, then look back and see what you missed.

Uses of Enzymes 1

Living cells use chemical reactions to produce <u>new materials</u>. Many of these reactions provide products which are <u>useful</u> to us. Here are <u>three</u> important examples:

Yeast in Brewing of Beer and Wine: Fermentation

1) <u>Yeast cells</u> convert <u>sugar</u> into <u>carbon dioxide</u> and <u>alcohol</u>.
2) They do this using the <u>enzyme</u> ZYMASE.
3) The main thing is to <u>keep the temperature just right</u>.
4) If it's <u>too cold</u> the enzyme won't work very <u>quickly</u>.
5) If it's <u>too hot</u> it will <u>destroy</u> the enzyme.
6) This biological process is called <u>fermentation</u> and is used for making alcoholic drinks like <u>beer and wine</u>.

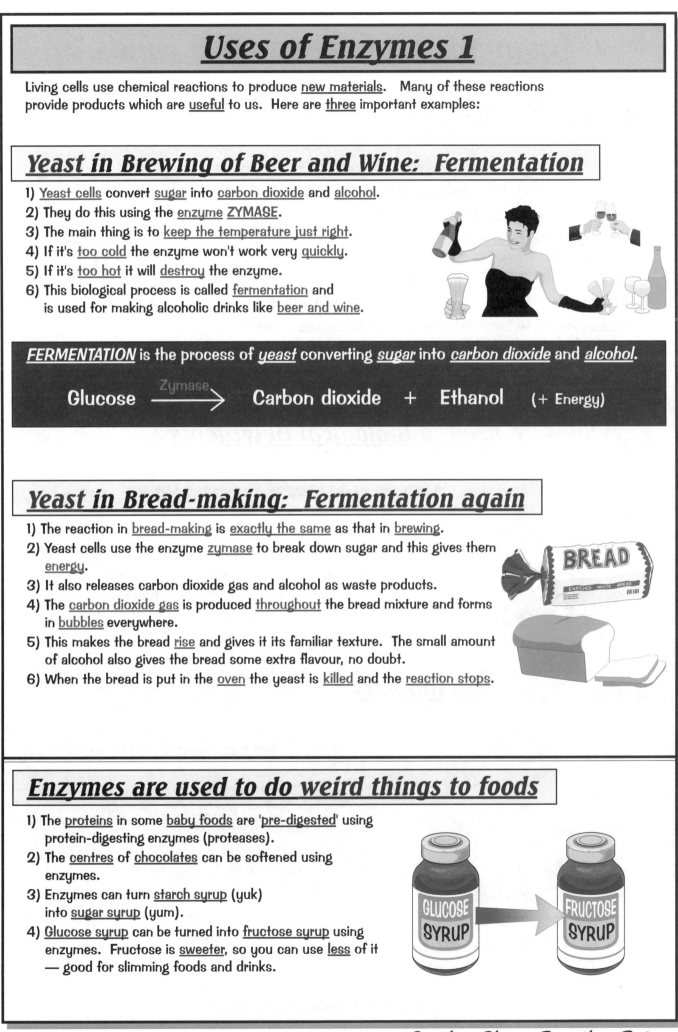

> <u>*FERMENTATION*</u> is the process of <u>*yeast*</u> converting <u>*sugar*</u> into <u>*carbon dioxide*</u> and <u>*alcohol*</u>.
>
> Glucose $\xrightarrow{\text{Zymase}}$ Carbon dioxide + Ethanol (+ Energy)

Yeast in Bread-making: Fermentation again

1) The reaction in <u>bread-making</u> is <u>exactly the same</u> as that in <u>brewing</u>.
2) Yeast cells use the enzyme <u>zymase</u> to break down sugar and this gives them <u>energy</u>.
3) It also releases carbon dioxide gas and alcohol as waste products.
4) The <u>carbon dioxide gas</u> is produced <u>throughout</u> the bread mixture and forms in <u>bubbles</u> everywhere.
5) This makes the bread <u>rise</u> and gives it its familiar texture. The small amount of alcohol also gives the bread some extra flavour, no doubt.
6) When the bread is put in the <u>oven</u> the yeast is <u>killed</u> and the <u>reaction stops</u>.

Enzymes are used to do weird things to foods

1) The <u>proteins</u> in some <u>baby foods</u> are 'pre-digested' using protein-digesting enzymes (proteases).
2) The <u>centres</u> of <u>chocolates</u> can be softened using enzymes.
3) Enzymes can turn <u>starch syrup</u> (yuk) into <u>sugar syrup</u> (yum).
4) <u>Glucose syrup</u> can be turned into <u>fructose syrup</u> using enzymes. Fructose is <u>sweeter</u>, so you can use <u>less</u> of it — good for slimming foods and drinks.

Uses of Enzymes 2

Yoghurt and Cheese making

1) Instead the milk is mixed with <u>specially grown cultures</u> of bacteria.

2) This mixture is kept at the <u>ideal temperature</u> for the bacteria and their enzymes to work.

3) For <u>yoghurt</u> this is <u>pretty warm</u> at about <u>45°C</u>.

4) The <u>yoghurt-making bacteria</u> convert <u>lactose</u> (the natural sugar found in milk), into <u>lactic acid</u>. This gives yoghurts their slightly <u>bitter</u> taste.

5) <u>Cheese</u> on the other hand matures better in <u>cooler conditions</u>.

6) <u>Various</u> bacterial enzymes can be used in <u>cheese making</u> to produce different <u>textures</u> and <u>tastes</u>.

Enzymes are used in Biological Detergents

1) <u>Enzymes</u> are the '<u>biological</u>' ingredients in biological detergents and washing powders.

2) They're mainly <u>protein-digesting</u> enzymes (proteases) and <u>fat-digesting</u> enzymes (lipases).

3) Because the enzymes attack <u>animal</u> and <u>plant</u> matter, they're ideal for removing <u>stains</u> like <u>food</u> or <u>blood</u>.

Using Enzymes in Industry takes a bit of fiddling

1) In an industrial process, the <u>temperature</u> and <u>pH</u> have to be right so the enzymes <u>aren't damaged</u>, and keep working for a long time.

2) The enzymes have to be kept from <u>washing away</u>. They can be mixed into <u>plastic beads</u>, or trapped in an <u>alginate bed</u> (seaweed mush).

3) Because enzymes work for a long time, you can <u>continually</u> pass chemicals over them to react, and tap off the product at the other end.

This page is just so easy — it's a blummin' picnic...

This is rapidly turning into a Domestic Science book. Anyway, you're expected to know all these details of making bread, wine, cheese, yoghurt, weird sugars and baby food, detergents, and the industrial bit. <u>Mini-essays again</u>, I'd say. <u>Enjoy</u>.

Simple Reversible Reactions

A <u>reversible reaction</u> is one which can go <u>in both directions</u>.
In other words the <u>products</u> of the reaction can be <u>turned back</u> into the original <u>reactants</u>.
Here are some <u>examples</u> you should know about in case they spring one on you in the Exam.

The Thermal decomposition of Ammonium Chloride

1) When <u>ammonium chloride</u> is <u>heated</u> it splits up into <u>ammonia gas</u> and <u>HCl gas</u>.
2) When these gases <u>cool</u> they recombine to form <u>solid ammonium chloride</u>.

$$NH_4Cl_{(s)} \rightleftharpoons NH_{3(g)} + HCl_{(g)}$$
Ammonium chloride   ammonia + hydrogen chloride
(white solid)   (colourless gases)

Cold Water

Ammonia and HCl gases

Solid ammonium chloride

Gentle Heat

This is a <u>typical</u> <u>reversible reaction</u> because the products <u>recombine</u> to form the original substance <u>very easily</u>.

You can do exactly the same experiment with <u>IODINE CRYSTALS</u>, which will turn to <u>purple iodine vapour</u> and then reform as <u>grey crystals</u> when they cool. However, do take note that this is <u>not</u> a reversible reaction, as such, but merely a <u>reversible physical process</u>.

Cold Water

Purple Iodine vapour

Grey Iodine crystals

Gentle Heat

The Thermal decomposition of hydrated copper sulphate

1) Good old dependable <u>blue copper(II) sulphate</u> crystals here again.
2) Here they're displaying their usual trick, but under the guise of a <u>reversible reaction</u>.

3) If you <u>heat them</u> it drives the water off and leaves <u>white anhydrous</u> copper(II) sulphate powder.

Water vapour

4) If you then <u>add</u> a couple of drops of <u>water</u> to the <u>white powder</u> you get the <u>blue crystals</u> back again.

The proper name for the <u>blue crystals</u> is <u>Hydrated Copper(II) sulphate</u>. "<u>Hydrated</u>" means "<u>with water</u>". When you drive the water off they become a white powder, <u>Anhydrous copper(II) sulphate</u>. "<u>Anhydrous</u>" means "<u>without water</u>".

Reacting Iodine with Chlorine to get Iodine Trichloride

There's quite a jolly <u>reversible reaction</u> between the mucky brown liquid of <u>iodine monochloride</u> (ICl), and nasty green <u>chlorine gas</u> to form nice clean yellow crystals of <u>iodine trichloride</u> (ICl$_3$).

$$ICl + Cl_2 \rightleftharpoons ICl_3$$

1) Which way the reaction goes depends on the <u>concentration of chlorine gas</u> in the air around.
2) <u>A lot of chlorine</u> will favour formation of the <u>yellow crystals</u>.
3) <u>A lack</u> of chlorine will encourage the crystals to <u>decompose</u> back to the horrid brown liquid.

Learn these simple reactions, then see what you know...

These reactions might seem a bit obscure but they're all mentioned in one syllabus or another, so any of them could come up in your Exam. There really isn't much to learn here. <u>Scribble it</u>.

Reversible Reactions in Equilibrium

A <u>reversible reaction</u> is one where the <u>products</u> can react with each other and <u>convert back</u> to the original chemicals. In other words, <u>it can go both ways</u>.

A ***REVERSIBLE REACTION*** IS ONE WHERE THE ***PRODUCTS*** OF THE REACTION CAN ***THEMSELVES REACT*** TO PRODUCE THE ***ORIGINAL REACTANTS***

$$A + B \rightleftharpoons C + D$$

Reversible Reactions will reach Dynamic Equilibrium

1) If a reversible reaction takes place in a <u>closed system</u> then a state of <u>equilibrium</u> will always be reached.

2) <u>Equilibrium</u> means that the <u>relative (%) quantities</u> of reactants and products will reach a certain <u>balance</u> and stay there. "<u>A closed system</u>" just means that none of the reactants or products can <u>escape</u>.

3) It is in fact a <u>DYNAMIC EQUILIBRIUM</u>, which means that <u>the reactions are still taking place</u> in <u>both directions</u> but the <u>overall effect is nil</u> because the forward and reverse reactions <u>cancel each other out</u>. The reactions are taking place at <u>exactly the same rate</u> in both directions.

Dynamic Equilibrium

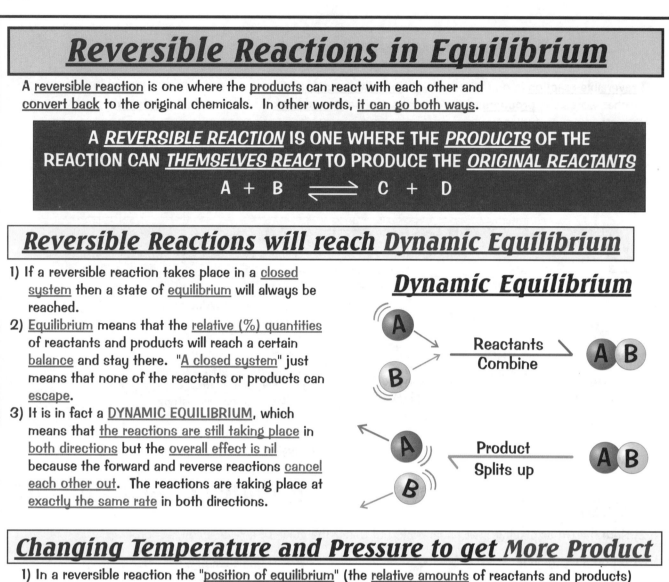

Reactants Combine

Product Splits up

Changing Temperature and Pressure to get More Product

1) In a reversible reaction the "<u>position of equilibrium</u>" (the <u>relative amounts</u> of reactants and products) depends <u>very strongly</u> on the <u>temperature</u> and <u>pressure</u> surrounding the reaction.

2) If we <u>deliberately alter</u> the temperature and pressure we can <u>move</u> the "position of equilibrium" to give <u>more product</u> and <u>less</u> reactants.

Two very simple rules for which way the equilibrium will move

1) All reactions are <u>exothermic</u> in one direction and <u>endothermic</u> in the other.
   If we <u>raise the temperature</u>, the <u>endothermic</u> reaction will increase to <u>use up</u> the extra heat.
   If we <u>reduce the temperature</u> the <u>exothermic</u> reaction will increase to <u>give out</u> more heat.

2) Many reactions have a <u>greater volume</u> on one side, either of <u>products</u> or <u>reactants</u>.
   If we <u>raise the pressure</u> it will encourage the reaction which produces <u>less volume</u>.
   If we <u>lower the pressure</u> it will encourage the reaction which produces <u>more volume</u>.

This is all summed up very nicely by Le Chatelier's Principle which states:

IF YOU ***CHANGE THE CONDITIONS***, THE ***POSITION OF EQUILIBRIUM*** WILL ***SHIFT*** TO ***OPPOSE*** THE CHANGE

(My guess is that Le Chatelier was French. Ask "Teach" whether you should know about him and his principle)

Learning/forgetting— the worst reversible of them all...

There's three sections here: the definition of a reversible reaction, the notion of dynamic equilibrium, and Le Chatelier's Principle. Make sure you can give a good rendition of all three.

The Haber Process Again

Other details of the Haber Process are given on P. 24.

The Haber Process is a controlled Reversible Reaction

The Equation is:

$$N_{2\,(g)} \quad + \quad 3H_{2\,(g)} \quad \rightleftharpoons \quad 2NH_{3\,(g)}$$

ΔH is -ve (see P. 79), i.e. the <u>forward</u> reaction is <u>exothermic</u>

Higher Pressure will Favour the Forward Reaction so build it strong...

1) On the <u>left side</u> of the equation there are <u>four moles</u> of gas ($N_2 + 3H_2$), whilst on the <u>right side</u> there are just <u>two moles</u> (of NH_3).

2) So any <u>increase in pressure</u> will favour the <u>forward reaction</u> to produce more <u>ammonia</u>. Hence the decision on pressure is <u>simple</u>. It's just set <u>as high as possible</u> to give the <u>best % yield</u> without making the plant <u>too expensive to build</u>. 200 to 350 atmospheres are typical pressures used.

(Applying Le Chatelier's principle gives the same result. The equilibrium moves in favour of more ammonia because that will reduce the volume of gas in the system, thereby trying to reduce the increase in pressure that we impose.)

Lower Temperature WOULD favour the forward Reaction BUT...

The reaction is <u>exothermic</u> in the forward direction, which means that <u>increasing</u> the temperature will actually move the equilibrium <u>the wrong way</u>, away from ammonia and more towards H_2 and N_2. <u>But they increase the temperature anyway</u>... this is the tricky bit so learn it real good:

LEARN THIS REAL WELL:

1) The <u>proportion</u> of ammonia at equilibrium can only be increased by <u>lowering</u> the temperature.
2) But instead they <u>raise</u> the temperature and accept a <u>reduced proportion</u> (or <u>yield</u>) of ammonia.
3) The reason is that the <u>higher</u> temperature gives a <u>much higher RATE OF REACTION</u>.
4) It's better to wait just <u>20 seconds</u> for a <u>10% yield</u> than to have to wait <u>60 seconds</u> for a <u>20% yield</u>.
5) Remember, the unused hydrogen, H_2, and nitrogen, N_2, are <u>recycled</u> so <u>nothing is wasted</u>.

The Iron Catalyst Speeds up the reaction and keeps costs down

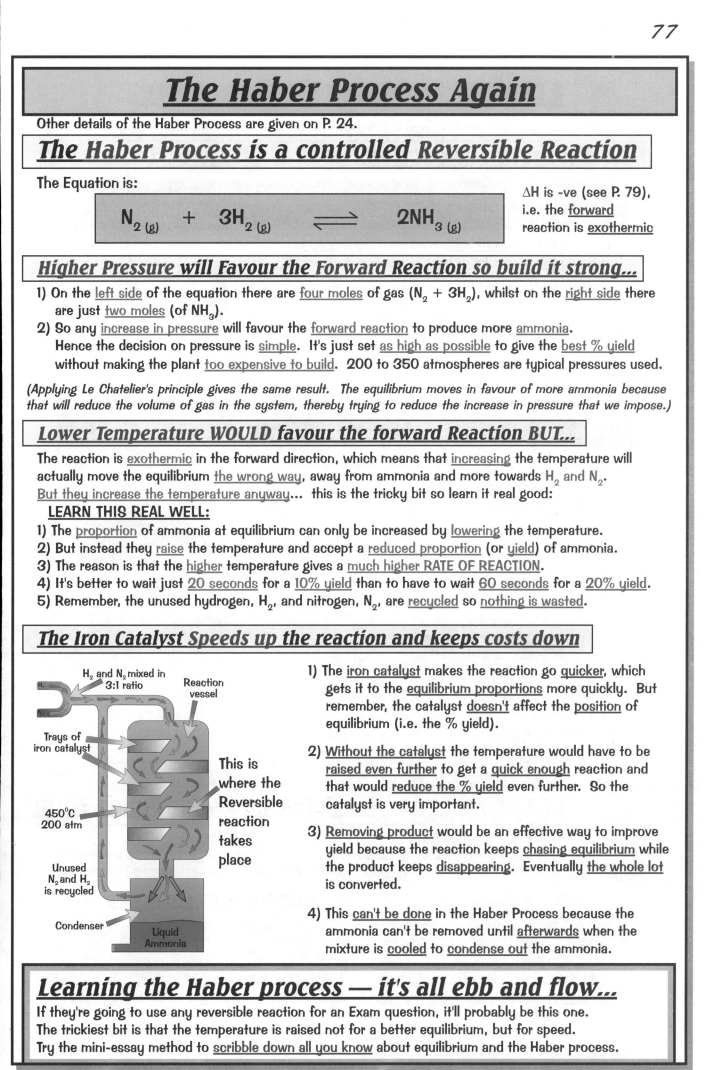

H₂ and N₂ mixed in 3:1 ratio

Reaction vessel

Trays of iron catalyst

This is where the Reversible reaction takes place

450°C 200 atm

Unused N₂ and H₂ is recycled

Condenser

Liquid Ammonia

1) The <u>iron catalyst</u> makes the reaction go <u>quicker</u>, which gets it to the <u>equilibrium proportions</u> more quickly. But remember, the catalyst <u>doesn't</u> affect the <u>position</u> of equilibrium (i.e. the % yield).

2) <u>Without the catalyst</u> the temperature would have to be <u>raised even further</u> to get a <u>quick enough</u> reaction and that would <u>reduce the % yield</u> even further. So the catalyst is very important.

3) <u>Removing product</u> would be an effective way to improve yield because the reaction keeps <u>chasing equilibrium</u> while the product keeps <u>disappearing</u>. Eventually <u>the whole lot</u> is converted.

4) This <u>can't be done</u> in the Haber Process because the ammonia can't be removed until <u>afterwards</u> when the mixture is <u>cooled</u> to <u>condense out</u> the ammonia.

Learning the Haber process — it's all ebb and flow...

If they're going to use any reversible reaction for an Exam question, it'll probably be this one. The trickiest bit is that the temperature is raised not for a better equilibrium, but for speed. Try the mini-essay method to <u>scribble down all you know</u> about equilibrium and the Haber process.

Energy Transfer in Reactions

Whenever chemical reactions occur, energy is usually transferred to or from the surroundings.

In an Exothermic Reaction, Heat is GIVEN OUT

> An **EXOTHERMIC REACTION** is one which **GIVES OUT ENERGY** to the surroundings, usually in the form of **HEAT** and usually shown by a **RISE IN TEMPERATURE**

1) The best example of an exothermic reaction is burning fuels. This obviously gives out a lot of heat — it's very exothermic.

2) Neutralisation reactions (acid + alkali) are also exothermic.

3) Addition of water to anhydrous copper(II) sulphate to turn it into blue crystals produces heat, so it must be exothermic.

ACID
Don't do it like this!
ALKALI
Steam

In an Endothermic Reaction, Heat is TAKEN IN

> An **ENDOTHERMIC REACTION** is one which **TAKES IN ENERGY** from the surroundings, usually in the form of **HEAT** and usually shown by a **FALL IN TEMPERATURE**

Endothermic reactions are less common and less easy to spot.
So LEARN these three examples, in case they ask for one:

1) *Photosynthesis* is endothermic — it takes in energy from the sun.

2) *Dissolving certain salts in water*
    e.g. 1) potassium chloride   2) ammonium nitrate

3) *Thermal decomposition*.
    Heat must be supplied to cause the compound to decompose.
    The best example is converting calcium carbonate into quicklime (calcium oxide — see P. 23).

Energy

Food

$$CaCO_3 \rightarrow CaO + CO_2$$

A lot of heat energy is needed to make this happen.
In fact the calcium carbonate has to be heated in a kiln and kept at about 800°C.
It takes almost 30,000kJ of heat to make 10kg of calcium carbonate decompose.
That's pretty endothermic I'd say, wouldn't you.

Energy Must Always be Supplied to Break bonds...
...and Energy is Always Released When Bonds Form

1) During a chemical reaction, old bonds are broken and new bonds are formed.
2) Energy must be supplied to break existing bonds — so bond breaking is an endothermic process.
3) Energy is released when new bonds are formed — so bond formation is an exothermic process.

BOND BREAKING - ENDOTHERMIC

Na Cl — Energy Supplied → Na + Cl
Strong Bond   Bond Broken

BOND FORMING - EXOTHERMIC

Mg + O ⟶ Mg O + Energy Released
          Strong Bond Formed

4) In an exothermic reaction, the energy released in bond formation is greater than the energy used in breaking old bonds.
5) In an endothermic reaction, the energy required to break old bonds is greater than the energy released when new bonds are formed.

Energy Transfer in Reactions

Energy Level Diagrams show if it's Exo- or Endo-thermic

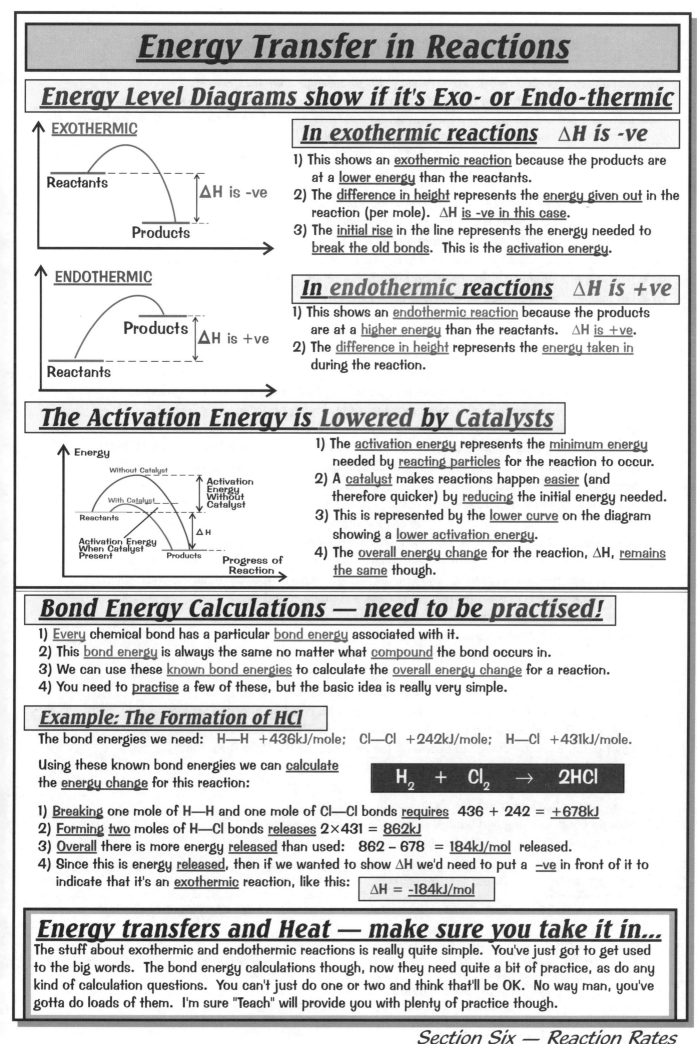

EXOTHERMIC

Reactants

Products

ΔH is -ve

In exothermic reactions ΔH is -ve

1) This shows an <u>exothermic reaction</u> because the products are at a <u>lower energy</u> than the reactants.
2) The <u>difference in height</u> represents the <u>energy given out</u> in the reaction (per mole). ΔH <u>is -ve in this case</u>.
3) The <u>initial rise</u> in the line represents the energy needed to <u>break the old bonds</u>. This is the <u>activation energy</u>.

ENDOTHERMIC

Products

ΔH is +ve

Reactants

In endothermic reactions ΔH is +ve

1) This shows an <u>endothermic reaction</u> because the products are at a <u>higher energy</u> than the reactants. ΔH <u>is +ve</u>.
2) The <u>difference in height</u> represents the <u>energy taken in</u> during the reaction.

The Activation Energy is Lowered by Catalysts

Energy

Without Catalyst

With Catalyst

Reactants

Activation Energy When Catalyst Present

Products

ΔH

Activation Energy Without Catalyst

Progress of Reaction

1) The <u>activation energy</u> represents the <u>minimum energy</u> needed by <u>reacting particles</u> for the reaction to occur.
2) A <u>catalyst</u> makes reactions happen <u>easier</u> (and therefore quicker) by <u>reducing</u> the initial energy needed.
3) This is represented by the <u>lower curve</u> on the diagram showing a <u>lower activation energy</u>.
4) The <u>overall energy change</u> for the reaction, ΔH, <u>remains the same</u> though.

Bond Energy Calculations — need to be practised!

1) <u>Every</u> chemical bond has a particular <u>bond energy</u> associated with it.
2) This <u>bond energy</u> is always the same no matter what <u>compound</u> the bond occurs in.
3) We can use these <u>known bond energies</u> to calculate the <u>overall energy change</u> for a reaction.
4) You need to <u>practise</u> a few of these, but the basic idea is really very simple.

Example: The Formation of HCl

The bond energies we need: H—H +436kJ/mole; Cl—Cl +242kJ/mole; H—Cl +431kJ/mole.

Using these known bond energies we can <u>calculate</u> the <u>energy change</u> for this reaction:

$$H_2 + Cl_2 \rightarrow 2HCl$$

1) <u>Breaking</u> one mole of H—H and one mole of Cl—Cl bonds <u>requires</u> 436 + 242 = <u>+678kJ</u>
2) <u>Forming two</u> moles of H—Cl bonds <u>releases</u> 2×431 = <u>862kJ</u>
3) <u>Overall</u> there is more energy <u>released</u> than used: 862 − 678 = <u>184kJ/mol</u> released.
4) Since this is energy <u>released</u>, then if we wanted to show ΔH we'd need to put a <u>−ve</u> in front of it to indicate that it's an <u>exothermic</u> reaction, like this: $\Delta H = \underline{-184\text{kJ/mol}}$

Energy transfers and Heat — make sure you take it in...

The stuff about exothermic and endothermic reactions is really quite simple. You've just got to get used to the big words. The bond energy calculations though, now they need quite a bit of practice, as do any kind of calculation questions. You can't just do one or two and think that'll be OK. No way man, you've gotta do loads of them. I'm sure "Teach" will provide you with plenty of practice though.

Revision Summary for Section Six

This section isn't too bad really. Well it's short for one thing. That always helps.
I suppose some of the stuff on Rates of Reaction and Equilibrium gets a bit chewy in places, but the rest is all a bit of a breeze really, isn't it? Anyway, here's some more of those nice easy questions which you enjoy so much. Remember, if you can't answer one, look at the appropriate page and learn it. Then go back and try them again. Your hope is that one day you'll be able to glide effortlessly through all of them — it's a nice trick if you can do it.

1) What are the three different ways of measuring the speed of a reaction?
2) What are the four factors which the rate of reaction depends on?
3) Explain how each of these four factors increase the *number of collisions* between particles.
4) What is the other aspect of collision theory which determines the rate of reaction?
5) Which is the only physical factor which affects this other aspect of the collisions?
6) What happens when hydrochloric acid is added to marble chips?
7) Give details of the two possible methods for measuring the rate of this reaction.
8) Sketch a typical set of graphs for either of these methods.
9) Describe in detail how you would test the effect on the reaction rate of
   a) finer particles of solid   b) stronger concentration of acid   c) temperature
10) What happens when sodium thiosulphate is added to HCl?   How is the rate measured?
11) Write down the equation for the decomposition of hydrogen peroxide.
12) What is the best way to increase the rate of this reaction?
13) What is the best way to measure the rate of this reaction? What will the graphs look like?
14) What is the definition of a catalyst? What does a catalyst do to the activation energy?
15) Name two specific industrial catalysts and give the process they are used in.
16) What are enzymes? Where are they made? Give three examples of their use by people.
17) Sketch the graph for enzyme activity vs temperature, indicating the temperatures.
18) What effect does freezing have on food? What happens when you thaw it out?
19) Give the word-equation for fermentation. Which organism and which enzyme are involved?
20) Explain what happens in brewing and bread-making.   What is the difference between them?
21) What kind of milk is needed for making cheese and yoghurt and why?
22) What gives yoghurt and cheese their flavour?
23) Explain how biological detergents work.
24) In what three ways are enzymes protected in industrial processes?
25) What is a reversible reaction? Describe three simple reversible reactions involving solids.
26) Explain what is meant by dynamic equilibrium in a reversible reaction.
27) How does changing the temperature and pressure of a reaction alter the equilibrium?
28) How does this influence the choice of pressure for the Haber Process?
29) What determines the choice of operating temperature for the Haber process?
30) What effect does the catalyst have on the reaction?
31) Give three examples of exothermic and three examples of endothermic reactions.
32) Draw energy level diagrams for these two types of reaction.
33) How do bond breaking and bond forming relate to these diagrams?
34) What are bond energies and what can you calculate from them?

Index

Index

Index

Index